WHADDYA MEAN
YOU CAN'T GO HOME AGAIN?

Who sez? Well, we say you can. Anybody who says you can't go home again is just plain simple-minded. No imagination.

You take in this boo[illegible] where this guy—Rhoades. [illegible]e is—starts tellin' abo[illegible] the terrific times they[illegible]ing store-keepers ou[illegible]monds and finagling Si[illegible]garettes and selling lemonade sp[illegible] vodka and all like that. Well, it kinda gets you right here, it's so real. Like it was yesterday. Only instead of having a wife or a boss to be afraid of you had a mother and father who'd clobber you. And then you could go out and beat up your brother or your sister, if you didn't have anybody smaller around.

Gee, it was wonderful. Remember? And the things you could write on fences! Zowie!

So anybody starts makin' cracks about how you can't go home, just show them this book, see?

Uncensored recollections of a man who remembers when boys were boys and went out and did something . . . anything . . . everything . . . "For connoisseurs of the Huckleberry Finn school of raffish humor."

—San Francisco *Examiner*

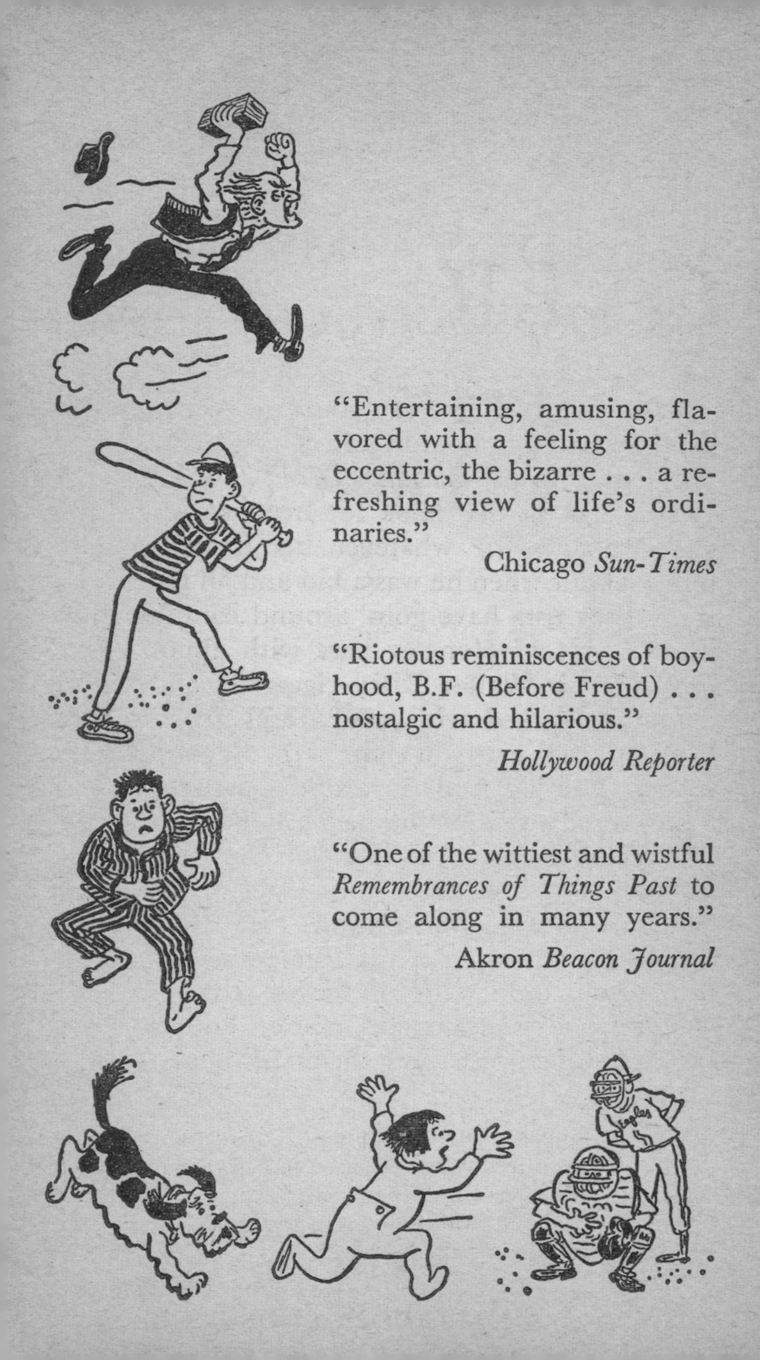

"Entertaining, amusing, flavored with a feeling for the eccentric, the bizarre . . . a refreshing view of life's ordinaries."

Chicago *Sun-Times*

"Riotous reminiscences of boyhood, B.F. (Before Freud) . . . nostalgic and hilarious."

Hollywood Reporter

"One of the wittiest and wistful *Remembrances of Things Past* to come along in many years."

Akron *Beacon Journal*

OVER THE FENCE IS OUT

JONATHAN RHOADES

Illustrated by
Robt Day

MB

A MACFADDEN BOOK

THIS BOOK IS THE COMPLETE
TEXT OF THE HARDCOVER BOOK

Dedication

This book is for Nelson Algren, Luis Aparicio, Jean Beliveau, Nick Blatchford, Robert Boyle, Walter Bradbury, Marlon Brando, Ray Brennan, Joe David Brown, Charles and Julia Campbell, Eula and Trip Child, Nelson Fox, George Chaplin, Dick Clurman, Ed Darby, Robert Day, Larry Fanning, Bill Furth, Arthur Goldberger, Charles Goren, T George Harris, Hugh Hefner, Serrell Hillman, Huston Horn, Sam Huff, Emmet Hughes, Leon Jaroff, Dick Johnston, James Philip Keene, Charles Kligerman, André Laguerre, Robert Lancaster, Jack Leonard, Tex Maule, Burt Meyers, Hugh Moffett, Hoke Norris, Mark Perlberg, Billy Pierce, Jacques Plante, Ed Reingold, Frank Rhoades (no relation), Jon Rinehart, Roy Rowan, Tom Sancton, Mort Sharnik, Jim Shepley, Larry Sizer, A. C. Spectorsky, Jerry Tax, Jack Tibby, Morrie Werner, Herm Weiskopf, Marvin Zim, Herb Zimmerman,

and

Judy, Jack, Susan, Lefty, Alan, Tippy, Evan, and Barrie.

A MACFADDEN BOOK . . . 1963

MACFADDEN BOOKS are published by
MACFADDEN-BARTELL CORPORATION
205 East 42nd Street, New York 17, New York

Library of Congress Catalog Card Number: 61-15356

1

The Greatness fo My Father and Other Myths

My father was the world's greatest automobile driver, baseball player, retread shop manager, horse handicapper, joketeller, bird identifier, and anything else you would care to mention. You search your memory, you say? And you cannot remember anyone named Harvey Rhoades in connection with any of the above talents? No, you cannot, because my father was also great in terms of modesty and self-effacement. He did not tootle his own kazoo.

Of course, every kid thinks his father is the greatest. The difference is, my father *was*. To give you an idea, let us study Father's actions at our ball games. To begin with, you should know that Father had been a professional ballplayer years before. (Modestly, he once explained to me that he had been a relief pitcher for the St. Louis Cardinals, nothing more. He said this because he wanted me to have pride in him. In point of actual fact, he had had a tryout with a semipro team in Selma, Alabama. My father didn't make the team. But aside from that, his story about playing for the Cardinals was true.)

He used to show up at our sand-lot games now and then, and two or three times we had to press him into service when the regulation nine men failed to show. Now you can just imagine the temptation this would be for the average full-grown man playing with a bunch of kids nine, ten, and eleven years old. What a temptation to whack the cover off the lousy pitching of some poor little kid! What a temptation to whirl and pirouette at second base, making the perfect pivot, and snap off a powerful throw to double up some stubby-legged little kid at first!

But this is where my father's greatness came in. He did none of these things. He played quietly and decently, without showboating, without making any of us feel inferior. He realized what a delicate thing the growing ego is. So every now and then he would make an "error," or he would strike out. I will admit: At first I didn't understand, and I was ashamed of him. But one day it all came clear. We were walking home from a game and I asked him how come he made four errors and went 0-for-6

at the plate, including three strike outs, and cost us the ball game with his lousy playing.

"Sonny," he said, "there is more to life than winning or losing a ball game. How do you think those kids would feel if I went out there and played my best?"

"Gee," I said. "I don't know."

"Do you think they'd have any fun if I hit a home run every time up or if I never made an error? Wouldn't that make them feel awful?"

"You mean you make errors . . ."

"Now, now," Father said. "I think we've talked enough," and he smiled a tiny, modest smile. Father never stood so tall as at that moment. Later I saw him play softball at a couple of company picnics, and I am proud and happy to say that Father did not show up his fellow employes, either, in spite of his background as a professional ballplayer.

Father was an all-around superior type (as I could document in a hundred different ways) and not only physically. He had brains. I cannot remember ever failing to get an answer from Father, no matter how advanced or complex my question. It now has dawned on me that Father's theory was that you could not deny a child an answer, *some* answer, *any* answer. I would ask, "What happened to dinosaurs?" and he would answer without a second's hesitation, "The saber-toothed tigers ate 'em up."

"What happened to the saber-toothed tigers?"

"They froze in the Ice Age."

"When was the Ice Age?"

"Thousands of years ago."

"Before Christ?"

"Yep. Ten million years before Christ, to be exact."

Kindly and brilliant soul that he was, Father could not bear to let us down. We asked, he answered. He also answered any and all questions thrown at him by the neighborhood kids, their parents, the grocer, traveling salesmen, farmers, and professors of Egyptology from the university. There is no instance in recorded or remembered history when Father ever said, "I don't know."

Nor was he ever to blame for anything wrong. Nor did he ever make a mistake. One night we were driving along South Street in our black 1933 Nash when suddenly there was a loud crash. We had sideswiped a streetcar. At least, I thought we had. But it turned out that the streetcar had sideswiped us. I learned this in court a few months after the accident. The transit company was suing Father. On the stand Father told how the trolley had swerved off the tracks and hit us and swerved back on the tracks. The lawyer shouted at Father, "Mr. Rhoades, it is a scientific impossibility for a trolley to leave the rails and return."

Said Father, "We are not interested in your theories, young man. We are interested in facts. And the fact is the trolley swerved."

I am aware that cynics would say that Father was making a self-serving, untruthful statement. But this would be unfair. Father's powers of self-hypnosis were more developed than the average person's, that's all. He could have convinced himself that he was Christy Mathewson and Battling Nelson, all rolled into one, and if you told him he was not Mathewson or Nelson, *you* would have been telling an untruth. And Father could have convinced you, too, just as he did the jury in that old accident case. By sheer strength of his own convictions and by his inflexible attitude of certainty, Father succeeded in creating in the jury's mind a reasonable doubt as to whether the trolley had swerved or not, and the result was that the transit company failed to collect. Father told me on the way home, "Today you have learned the greatness of the American system, Sonny. No matter what they tell you, never forget: *The truth will win out!*"

This was but one of Father's bizarre theories which were to be exploded later in my life. Another was that you could be thrown through the back window of a car if the driver braked suddenly.

I learned about this new law of physics when I was eight. My little sister, Susan, and my little brother, Charley, and I used to look out the back window of our car and pretend that other cars were chasing us. A car on our tail was called a ghost, and the name of the game was ghost-es, which is the childhood plural of ghost (similar childhood plurals are mask-es, desk-es, chest-es, and nest-es). Anyway, we were playing ghost-es one night when my father told us to stop and face the front. He said he was afraid we'd be thrown through the back window if he had to stop suddenly. I said, "No, we would go forward."

"Oh, yeh?" said Father. "Well, how do you explain all those pictures of people killed by being thrown out the back window?"

That was the way with Father. If you disagreed with him, he would claim that he had seen the proof of his position with his own eyes. And were you trying to say he had been seeing things? No, of course not, and therefore he won all arguments.

My mother had the perfect technique for him, and years later I realized it was the only way. When Father would make one of his illogical, unreasonable, and downright preposterous claims, Mother would say calmly, "I wouldn't be surprised."

I would hear Father say, "The reason goats eat cans is because they instinctively know that iron builds up their blood," or "In a couple of years, all your housework'll be done by robots"; and always Mother would answer, "I wouldn't be surprised."

I remember with crystal clarity my father's saying one Sunday afternoon, "Caroline! The Japanese have attacked Pearl Harbor!"

Mother never even looked up from the cookies she was cutting. "Well," she said, "I wouldn't be surprised."

But of course he had to be right sometimes.

2

You Gotta Be Patient with Parents

FATHER was always blind in the morning. He would waver down the steps like *Hamlet's* ghost, muttering unintelligibilities, while all of us kids would scatter before his path. Each time we would break in a new dog (which was about every six weeks), the first thing we would have to teach the animal was to get out of Father's path on that awful pre-breakfast stroll. Once we had a spitz which regularly used to head for the county line whenever Father's odyssey began; he had caught a bedroom slipper full in the nose one morning and no amount of explanation by my father later could soothe the dog's spirits.

Father would come bumbling down the stairs, and just as he rounded the "L" at the bottom, he would begin muttering, "Caroline, Caroline, where's a coffee?" (One morning he came down and muttered, "Nancy, Nancy, where's a coffee?" But that is another story, and

a highly dramatic one.) It never seemed to occur to Father that the coffee was always in the same place. My mother would grab him by the sleeve of his robe (which he usually had on backward or with the buttons misaligned) and lead him to the kitchen table.

There Father would sit, hands trembling,

eyes mere slits, head nodding toward his chest, while Mother set the cup before him. We kids would listen from our hiding places. Mother would say, "Here you are, Harvey, here you are." There would be a clink and a rattle, a few more clinks and rattles, and suddenly Father would be himself again. "Well, well, Caroline," we would hear him say. "That certainly is a good cup of coffee." We would all run into the kitchen to be greeted one by one, another crisis weathered.

Our kitchen was a warm, antiseptic place with a permanent background aroma of Bon Ami and Dutch Cleanser, SOS and ammonia, because my mother's main interest in life was keeping things spotlessly clean, and the kitchen most of all. Father claimed that she spent more money on cleaning materials than she did on food. She was always down on the floor, her knees on a little rubber mat, scrubbing away at some corner which already shone with cleanliness. We were not permitted to wear shoes into the kitchen; they were left outside, *à la Chinois,* in neat little rows.

Looking back, I realize now what nightmares we kids must have caused Mother. I remember her working all day Saturday and on into the late night to clean up a perfect set of catprints, left by a scurrying tom whose paws had been dipped in ink by Susan, age four. To this day I do not understand that cat's choice of an escape route: across the living-room rug, over the sofa, up the curtains, back down the curtains, across the rug, and out the front door. I can say one thing with certainty, however: That cat was traveling *fast,* and the proof is that he left a single inkprint on the ceiling.

Mother also became disturbed when Susan skated on the kitchen floor. Susan did not wear roller skates; instead, she tied cantaloupe rinds to her shoes and skated across the linoleum in slick, noiseless arcs. The first time it happened, Mother was fairly tolerant, but she must have raised an awful din the second (and last) time, because Mrs. Gottlieb asked me the next day what Mother had been so upset about. Mrs. Gottlieb lived eleven doors down the street, and was slightly hard of hearing.

Once I set the kitchen on fire with my chemistry set, and the blaze left a long, brown scar across the white ceiling. My father commented nervously on how ugly this was, and Mother agreed. "One thing about fire," she added quickly, "it leaves a nasty stain, but it's a *clean* stain." The distinction was important to Mother.

Perhaps I should mention one other parental idiosyncrasy, this one shared by both. They had an absolute and acute inability to come to grips with the world of nature. Not that they didn't keep trying, although Mother said frequently that we should move to the twenty-fifth floor of one of those new apartment buildings and see if field mice and rats and squirrels and cockroaches could climb *that* high.

We didn't live far enough out in the country to be overrun by wild animals, yet we lived far enough out to have a few. One summer a thieving animal put our house on his beat, and nightly he would rattle the lid off our garbage pail, leaving a mess of empty cans, discarded meat wrappers, and denuded bones under our back porch. Now a lot of people would have thought this was cute and woodsy, but Father, prodded by Mother, took the whole thing as a personal affront. He lay in wait night after night for that mysterious intruder, and night after night the animal stayed away. Then Father, eyes bloodshot and bones weary from sitting up till 3 A.M., would take a cat nap, and the animal would strike. This went on for a full month.

Then one night Father was awakened by the crash of an overturning garbage can. He shook my mother awake and announced fuzzily, "Caroline! Wake up! I got that dirty little Boche son of a bitch right where I want him now." Down the hall crept Father in his standard sleeping paraphernalia: one T-shirt. He grabbed up my BB gun and his flashlight and padded out

the front door into the night. Skulking around a back corner of the house, he picked up two red-glowing eyes in his beam, and then made out the shadowy figure of a skinny raccoon.

Neither adversary acknowledged the presence of the other for long seconds. Then Father quickly lifted the gun, sighted down the flashlight, and fired. The raccoon continued to crunch away on a used ear of corn; Father had neglected to load the gun. Fumbling in the dark, he succeeded in this arduous task while the raccoon ambled around the corner of the house. Father followed. And so they went, around and around, with Father squeezing off a total of three rounds, all of them wild and none of them packing enough punch to make a half-inch dent in a bowl of whipped cream. As one final insult, the raccoon would reach out a paw every time they passed the garbage pail and grab a bone or a cooky remnant to sustain him on the next lap around the house.

I will say this for Father: Once committed to the task, he never gave up. He flung the gun; he picked up a rock and heaved it, missing the coon but putting a nice scar on our 1936 Pontiac; he reversed his field neatly and tried to catch the animal coming around the other way. Now it became a battle of intelligences, and Father would have won, if he had been left on his own. But just when he was crouched in front of the house, inching across the grass, about to pounce on that coon huddled around the corner, Mother flipped on our big front-porch light, and the whole private tableau entered the public domain. Father stood stock-still and blinked his eyes once. When he heard Mrs. Crawford scream from her upstairs window across the street, he realized he was not exactly dressed for the Easter Parade, and he bolted into the house. I tell you, it took many long hours to explain the whole thing to the satisfaction of the police department.

It turned out that Father had more long-range tenacity than that raccoon. The animal never came back, probably figuring that there were easier places to make a living than a neighborhood populated by hysterics. But Father set about perfecting himself as a marksman, so that he would be ready for nature's next assult. With a high-powered .22 varmint gun he practiced for hours in the basement, firing into a sandbag against the wall. Soon he realized that he must shoot at greater distances. The longest straight-line distance possible in our house (he didn't dare practice outside) was about sixty feet, running from the front vestibule, through the living room, down the hall, along one side of the kitchen, and into the pantry. Father rigged up a warning system composed of ropes and flags and pulleys. He had only to pull a single rope, and the red banners snapped into line at all entrances to the firing area, and they became out of bounds. At first we felt like those infantrymen who must crawl on their stomachs under a barrage of real machine-gun fire in training. But when we got used to the system it was really quite relaxing. I would be doing my homework at the desk next to the hall door, and Mother would be cooking, and Susan and Charlie would be playing Chinese checkers, and Father's bullets would go whining toward the target just a few feet from all of us. Whenever we absolutely had to cross the danger area, we would simply holler, "Cease fire!" and Father usually would halt.

You might think the whole routine was one grandiose waste of time, since the raccoon never returned, but Father's marksmanship eventually came in handy. He got so good that he could pick off a perched pigeon or starling at fifty yards, and thus our neighborhood was kept clear of infestations of these dirty birds and Father became quite a folk hero on our street. But he could never hit a bat on the wing, and it grieved him, because Father feared bats more than any other creatures. It was a fear that bordered almost on the psychopathic, yet it was not uncommon in a generation nurtured on the idea that bats will fly into the hair and make an awful tangle. When Father walked at twilight, his hand would keep flying back and forth to his hair, as if he were saying, "Hmmmmm, no bats yet!" He used to take a terrible kidding from Uncle Harry about this.

"Why you so afraid of bats?" Uncle Harry asked one night in front of the whole family circle.

"I'm not afraid of them," Father said quickly, his hand instinctively reaching to his hairline. "It's just . . . It's just . . . there's an old French saying that it's bad luck to have a bat in your house."

"As usual, you got it wrong," said Uncle Harry, the trace of a wry smile on his face. "The saying is that it's bad luck to have an *elephant* in your house," and he went cackling off to bed.

Not long after this riposte Father got even with Uncle Harry, and then some. On Halloween night, 1938, Father was reading the sports pages and I was sprawled on the rug reading Buck Rogers and Hairbreadth Harry, while the radio played in the background. Both Father and I perked up at the introduction of one of our favorite programs, *Mercury Theater on the Air,* followed by the announcement that tonight's production would be "War of the Worlds." Father and I put down our papers to listen. The program began with a "weather report," then there was some "dance music," and suddenly the announcer broke in with a "news bulletin" announcing that creatures from outer space were landing in New Jersey and spreading across the countryside spraying heat-rays. It sounded so real; if Father and I hadn't known it was Orson Welles, we'd have sworn this was the end.

Just then Uncle Harry came down the stairs.

Father waggled a finger at him, said, "Shhhhhh, Harry, a news bulletin."

Over the loud-speaker came an authoritative voice "on the scene of the landings," reporting that a Martian "cylinder" was landing.

"What?" said Uncle Harry.

"Shhhhhh," said Father.

The anouncer went on: "Good heavens, something's wriggling out of the shadow like a grey snake. Now it's another one and another. . . . I can see the thing's body. It's large as a bear and it glistens like wet leather. But that face. . . ."

"What the hell's going on here?" demanded Uncle Harry.

Answered Father, in a voice totally disinterested and nonchalant, "We're being attacked by Martians. But I wouldn't worry about it, Harry. They must be a good twenty miles away."

"My God," said Uncle Harry.

The announcer went on: "It's indescribable. I can hardly force myself to keep looking at it. The eyes are black and gleam like a serpent. The mouth is V-shaped with saliva dripping from its rimless lips that seem to quiver and pulsate."

Uncle Harry scooted upstairs just as the "news bulletin" was interrupted by "an announcement from the Secretary of the Interior," who intoned: "Citizens of the nation: I shall not try to conceal the gravity of the situation that confronts the country."

Uncle Harry raced back downstairs carrying a small traveling bag and his chess set and was out the front door before Father and I realized what was happening.

"Harry! Harry!" Father shouted. "It's all in fun! Come back! Harreeeeeeeeeeee!"

But Uncle Harry was around the corner and gone. (It turned out that he hitchhiked a ride, told the driver what was happening, and the two of them drove seventy-five miles into the mountains before learning the truth.)

Father and I decided to stay on the front porch and see if there was any more neighborhood reaction. There proved to be three separate incidents in our area, not counting Uncle Harry's flight, but there were thousands in the entire country. The worst reaction in our neighborhood was by old Mrs. Kearney, who ran into the Elkin's house down the street and laid out Mrs. Elkins with the butt end of an axe. The two had been feuding for years, and Mrs. Kearney wanted to get in the last blow before the arrival of the Martians. (Mrs. Elkins recovered nicely with the aid of a silver plate in her head, but has ever since been ordered to remain inside the house during electrical storms.)

An elderly gentleman from the end of the

block took off like a sprinter, white mane flying straight out behind him, shouting, "Our time has come! Our time has come!" He had been predicting the end of the world every day for years, and now he was more or less happy that his prediction had come true and he could put his master plan into effect. He was found by police hours later, beating his way through the woods on hands and knees. He explained that he was searching for two of every kind of animal, and that his mission was terribly important, and that they shouldn't bother him. But they bothered him anyway.

Father and I witnessed the third incident in our neighborhood with our own eyes, and it was a rare thrill for me, as it represented my first opportunity for an all-over look at the undressed female body. She was a chubby woman, new to our street, and she came barreling down the sidewalk wearing only a cloche hat. Various parts of her were flying in all directions as she passed Father and me. She slowed slightly, waved, and said a tentative but not unfriendly "Hi!" Then she roared on down the street and out of sight. I never did find out her name. She moved a few days later.

3

The Star Pitcher

We played baseball in a big empty lot surrounded by houses and streets. If you hit the ball over the fence, it would go down the sewer or onto the front porch of some old witch who already had a bucket of confiscated baseballs in her basement, gathering mold. So in our game the first rule was: Over the fence is out. (I know a man named Bradbury who played his childhood baseball on a leveled-off mountaintop in South Dakota. Over the fence was out there, too, because the ball would roll down the mountain and they would never see it again. Bradbury is a bore to watch baseball games with. Any time there's a home run, he has to tell you how *he* once hit a ball a mile and a half.)

This over-the-fence-is-out rule used to set up terrible conflicting forces in the minds of our good hitters. The fence was 'way out there at the hundred-forty-foot mark. If they really teed off (as, for example, when I was pitching), they would clear the fence and be out. If they didn't quite connect, the ball might hit off the fence for a triple, but it also might be caught by an outfielder. I always figured this is why none of the kids in our neighborhood ever made the big leagues; they had a subconscious fear of hitting the ball too hard, and making out. I know for a fact that Bud Lewins almost lost a game for our junior-high-school team once; he smacked the ball over the fence of the school athletic field with two men on, and he flang his bat twenty feet in the air and said, "Ah, hell," before somebody on the bench hollered, "Run around the bases, Bud. It cleared the fence." For a second, he had thought he was back on the vacant lot.

I am in possession of a box score from one of those games, played when we were all about eleven, and it tells the story of the greatest athletic day in my life. It's funny how the best things often happen when you least expect it. I wasn't even supposed to pitch that day. Mostly I was the manager, because my father was a big Athletics fan and he used to supply me with scuffed-up baseballs once in a while. On this particular day we were playing the Highland Avenue Eagles, and they were hot stuff. (Three of them later made our high-school team, and one of them, Shorty Wilkes, went all the way to

Class-C baseball before they found out he could be had high and inside.) Fred Savarese was supposed to pitch for us, but he was on probation in geography and had to stay home to study. Our other pitcher, Coffee Parks, had started warming up for the game at 9:30 in the morning. By the time the game started at 2:00 in the afternoon he had a sore arm. So I had to leave it up to me.

Lewins was our catcher in those days, and before the game we discussed the signs. "One finger is a fast ball," he said, and I nodded knowingly. "Two is a hook, three is a drop, four is a roundhouse, five is a slow ball, and a fist means a inshoot." Luckily this was before the days of the knuckle ball and the slider and the back-up scroogie and other silly pitches. We did have the change-up, but we called it a slow ball. We had the slow change-of-pace curve, but we called it a roundhouse. We had no fork ball. To be perfectly honest, we really didn't have any of the other pitches, either, except the slow ball. But we liked to think we could throw them all, and that's why the catcher's signs. It was a sort of mass hallucination.

I refer now to the official box score, kept by my sister. It shows that I walked the first three men. This was to be expected, as I had had very short notice and hadn't had time to put Sloan's Liniment on my arm before the game. Sloan's Liniment always helped my control. The Eagles' clean-up man was the guy who later played Class C, and he knocked it over the fence in dead center. The ball bounced off the Nelsons' front porch and back onto the field, but under the rules it was just a long out. I was settling down.

The next man up hit a hard shot to me. Since I was regularly a shortstop, with a sterling .674 fielding average on the season, this ball presented no problem for me. I gobbled it up and fired it to the catcher for the cinch force-out at home, but for some reason or other Buddy Lewins had run down to back up first and there was nobody at home plate to take my perfect peg. I ran in, retrieved the ball, and threw it over the third baseman's head. The left fielder grabbed the ball on the first bounce and flung it over the backstop, and four runs were in.

I cursed the lousy support and went back to work with grim determination. It's one out and we're behind four-nothing. But the bases are empty, and things could be worse. The number-six batter drills a ball through the box into center-field; the second baseman just barely gets a glove on it; so I make it an error on him. (I forgot to tell you, I was also official scorer, and I went by a simple rule of thumb: If you missed a ball that Charley Gehringer would have got, it was an error.)

So then I walk two more guys, being still upset by the lack of support behind me. That brings up their pitcher with the bases loaded again. He hits a perfect double-play ball about twenty feet to the left of the shortstop, but that moron doesn't even get a glove on it. The ball goes between the outfielders and rolls all the way to the fence, and three runs score. I award errors to the shortstop and the left and center fielders.

Now the Highland Avenue bench starts up that stupid chant to the tune of the bugle call, "Assembly":

There's a pitcher in the box with a head like an ox.
Take him out, take him out, take him out, take him out.

and

The pitcher's in the air and the catcher needs a chair.
Take him out, take him out, take him out, take him out.

Very clever.

But the smiles were wiped off their silly faces when the next batter hit it over the fence in right. That made two out. I walked the next two batters on lousy calls by the umpire (who was regularly a pitcher for the Highland Avenue Eagles), and Lewins waddled out to the mound. "I think you're losing your stuff," he said.

"Whose ball we using?" I asked.

"Yours."

"Then I ain't losing my stuff."

I was right. The next batter hit a whistling line drive down the first-base line at Ducky Levinson. Ducky had two choices: He could catch the ball or he could have a fractured skull. He caught the ball, and we were out of the woods.

I will not bore you with the other details of the game. All the nuances and finesse and fine points were wrapped up in that first inning. We scored three runs in our half, but they came right back and took advantage of our lousy fielders and scored two more runs in the second. The final score was 19-11, favor them.

I was walking home with Lewins and Teddy Jepson, and my sister was straggling twenty feet behind, as usual, carrying the official box score. Suddenly it hit me. "Lemme see that thing!" I said to my sister. I checked up and down the columns. "Holy mackerel!" I shouted. "Holy cow! Look at that! What a incredulous performance!"

Jep and Buddy crowded around, and I showed them the miracle. It was right down there in black and white. I had pitched a no-hitter! In five full innings I had pitched to fifty-eight batters, walking nineteen, striking out one, and getting fourteen others out, six them on balls over the fence. Behind me on the field, my team had committed thirty-one errors.

But it was a no-hitter, no doubt about it. Which is why I still have that yellowing old box score.

I remember that night when my father came home. "Father," I said, catching him in the driveway. "I pitched a no-hitter against Highland Avenue today!"

His face lit up. I know he had always considered me an athletic failure up to then. "A no-hit, no-run game!" he said. "Sonny, that's a real achievement."

"Well, it wasn't exactly a no-hit, no-run game. They got nineteen runs, but I had lousy support."

"Oh," he said. "I see. They missed two of their extra points, eh? Well, that's all right. You'll do better next time."

I couldn't figure that one out. How can you do better than a no-hitter?

4

Wild Dogs I Have Known

WE once had a dog named Rover, which only goes to show what a sweet, naïve decade the thirties were. Who would dare today to name a dog Rover? In these supersophisticated times dogs have to be named Neal, or Cadwallader's Tsetse Fly of Westport, or Susie, or Peter B. Collins Jr., or something like that. I know a family in Beverly Hills that has a dog named William and a son named Prince.

When I was a kid there was a short list of acceptable names for dogs, and you had to make your selection from the list or face neighborhood ostracism. For females, you chose Lady, Lassie, Princess, Toby, Trixie, Dutchess, Queenie, or Boots. Males were Rex, Pal, Laddie, Prince, Blackie, King, Duke, Muggs, Fido, Spot, Tray, or Rags. These lists applied to all breeds except Pekingese and chows, which were named (regardless of sex) Ching, Ling, Ping, Ming, or Sing. In my whole childhood there was only one dog who was named outside of these rules. He was a Doberman pinscher named Count Wernher von Holschwitzen, who moved into our neighborhood in the late 1930's, but whose owner soon shot himself. Our parents shook their heads knowingly. In those days no well-adjusted person would have named a dog Count Wernher von Holschwitzen. Nowadays, of course, it would be considered just as nutty to name a dog Rover.

But we did, as I started to say, and a considerable dog he was, too. He had a huge head which bespoke German shepherd blood, a low short body like a bulldog, and a total lack of tail. You would see him coming around a corner and you would expect to see a German shepherd, but by the time the head had come fully into sight, it seemed that the whole rest of the dog had already gone past. He was all head, and his head was all teeth. Mother didn't want him around. She said he had no feelings for any of us. Father disagreed. He said the dog liked us very much, preferably medium-rare.

We got Rover as a puppy, and he was a cute little thing, dragging his huge head around the floor and wagging his rump at us. But by the time he was two months old, his whole personality underwent an evil change. I think it happened when Rover discovered his teeth; a sort of power madness set in. He chewed clear through the garage wall while he was still a puppy. He used to nip through the soles of our shoes. He dug back-yard holes big enough to stock with muskellunge. When Father stepped into one of the holes and wrenched a knee, he announced that Rover had to go.

But this was no simple task. The word was out, and there were almost no takers. Also, Rover had developed a strong liking for the flavors to be found around our house. On those few occasions when we got somebody to take him, the dog would wind up at our back door the next night, dragging a long chain with a door attached to it or a length of fence post he had ripped loose. Once he chewed through a half-inch lead pipe and walked three miles back home, showing his happiness on arrival by eating my brother Charley's football, including the bladder.

This went on for the better part of a year, during which time our popularity—never especially high—went down in the neighborhood. Once one of Father's old school friends, passing through town, announced that he liked the dog's looks and sure would admire to take him out to his farm in Jersey to learn some hunting. This was a preposterous idea; if there was one thing Rover did not have to learn, it was hunting. But my father jumped at the opportunity; the farm was fifty miles away. "If you want him, George, you take him," Father said. "My little boys'll get over it, and I'd like to see the dog happy."

That night we all relaxed at dinner; all, that is, except Father. He kept looking at his watch. "It's too good to be true, Caroline," he said. "I figure George'll bring him back right about the middle of the dessert."

Father was wrong. It was just at the *beginning* of dessert when we heard the screeching of brakes in front of the house, followed by a terrible caterwauling and screaming. Father and Charley and I ran out to see what was happening (though we had a fair idea). It turned out that George had opened the back of the truck to let Rover out. Then George raced for the cab and threw the truck into gear, but not before Rover, in one superdog jump, had made it through the window and now was chewing over poor George. It took three of us to drag him off, whereupon George, without even saying thanks, sped down the road. "That dog got five of my chickens and a duck!" he shouted into his slip stream. We heard him yell something, too, about a prize Hampshire hog, but we were unable to make this out as the taillights, tilting wildly, vanished around the corner.

This was enough for Father, and he proclaimed loudly that he was going to find out what ailed this animal if it took fifty years. He drove Rover to Dr. Carroll, our veterinarian, and Dr. Carroll, after making certain tests and taking all sorts of risks, said it was his opinion that Rover was not a dog at all, but a subspecies of wolverine. There was nothing to be done for the dog, short of assassination, but Mother frowned on that and quoted the Commandments. Father tried to explain that the Commandments applied only to humans, but Mother was adamant, and so we had to put up with Rover for another four or five months, until somebody in the neighborhood poisoned him. We never found out who did it, and we always felt bad about that. We didn't know whom to thank.

We had a lot of other dogs, but we never seemed to be able to get along with them, and vice versa. I remember a beautiful boxer named Duke, whom I have viewed with more and more suspicion as the years have waned. Duke had an annoying habit of waggling his behind as he walked. Nor did I like the way he would look up at us archly out of the corner of his eyes, his head tilted at a slight angle. And his walk, I swear, was mincing. It is plain to me now (though it was anything but plain then) that Duke was a homosexual, the victim of an unfulfilled relationship with his mother or something. Now I am well aware that all dogs are promiscuous and unpredictable sexually; we once had a bitch named Lady II who had to be locked in the cellar whenever the Sisters of the Scriptures met, because she had a mad physical crush on Mrs. A. Fotheringham Millard and didn't care who knew it. But the strange thing about Duke was that he was not promiscuous. He was completely faithful to the Warburtons' Alsatian, Prince, and to absolutely nobody else. He would spend hours on the Warburtons' steps, baying for Prince to come out. He brought bones to Prince, real bones with shreds of red meat still clinging to them. I'm sure he would have brought candy and flowers if he had known how to get them. It was embarrassing to have a big boxer dog acting like such a sissy, and I'm just glad my brother and sister and I didn't know the truth.

I don't know whether my father ever suspected that the dog was a nance, but I do know that he once took Duke to a kennel to cause some puppies. Two days later my father brought him back home, and I heard my mother ask if Duke had "liked her."

"Yeh," Father said disgustedly, "but only in a clean, decent way."

Father just did not have a green thumb with dogs, though he would never admit it. We had a whole series of "working dogs" who couldn't have found birds in a rookery. One of them, a pointer named Boots, used to run around our neighborhood making perfect points on cats, turtles, and tricycles; but if she ever went on point in the field, nobody was there to see it. We had an Irish setter who used to drive Father nearly berserk. As Father explained once, "He points the birds perfectly. He flushes them and I knock them down. Off he goes on the retrieve. Five minutes later he's back, licking his chops. I wouldn't mind that, but does he have to belch?"

After years of horrible failures with dogs, Father developed one of the most interesting behavioral theories of his era. It was Father who discovered that dogs will respond better, react faster, learn more thoroughly, and obey more completely if they can be made to think of their master as *a large dog*. Dogs will listen to their own kind, Father explained, when they will ignore humans. You had to learn to talk to them. To this end, Father developed a whole set of dog-sounds which I must admit had the ring of reality to them. We owned, at the time, two female "baggles" (half-Basset and half-beagle), and they combined the worst characteristics—stubbornness, stupidity, noisiness—of both breeds. But Father was able to get a surprising amount of coöperation out of them

by using his dog-sounds. When they damaged the second-hand Oriental rug, Father pointed to the spot and growled menacingly. They never used *that* rug again. When they retrieved sticks or rubber balls, Father barked cheerfully, thus communicating his pride to the animals. When one of them cut her foot, Father whimpered along with her, and both dogs seemed to appreciate and understand the sympathy. Father was making good pets out of those dogs.

But they had one remaining bad habit which nothing seemed to correct. They would come to the front door and scratch to get in. Father tried everything, and finally decided that only a reign of animal terror would break them before they had clawed the whole front door to tatters. Whenever he heard the scratching, Father would vault out of his chair, rip open the door, and emit an ear-splitting roar of jungle anger. I can hear it now, rumbling out of Father's throat, gaining power in his larynx, rushing into his mouth, and then bursting into the air—ggggrrrRRRRAAAAHHHHHHHHHHH! ! !—like a monster lion.

My, how those poor little dogs would run, yelping and screaming, when they heard Father roar! Sometimes we wouldn't see them for three days, but then hunger and habit and stupidity would drive them back to the front door, back to the warm place where that strange big dog lived and ruled and growled. And who knows that they wouldn't finally have learned not to scratch on the door, if only Father had kept up his act? But one night the whole routine came tumbling down.

Father was sitting in his leather chair, reading the *Evening Public Ledger*, when that familiar *scratch-scratch* came from the front door. All in one beautifully coördinated motion Father bounded across the room, yanked the door open, and

ggggrrrRRRRAAAAHHHHHHHed

into the night. But it wasn't the dogs. It was a Girl Scout, scratching for the doorbell so she could make her annual pitch for cookies. The poor little thing ran screaming all the way

home, and it was a month before Father could make the child, her parents, the judiciary, and a hastily formed committee of townspeople see the truth. For a long time after that we would sec people driving slowly past our house on summer nights, and we would hear someone in the car say, "There, right there, that's the place. . . ."

5

The Great Beer Bust

THERE has never been a drinking problem in the Rhoades family. I don't mean to sound goody-goody about it, but the facts are there. The Rhoadeses like to hoist a few, but they somehow never turn into alcoholics. As I told my pal Amby Molle one day when we were both in the late teens, "My father drinks at least one beer or one highball every day of his life and yet I've never seen him drunk or even a little high." Amby's response was, "How could you tell?" which I, of course, ignored.

But for a family of nonproblem drinkers, we certainly had a lot of experiences involving beer and alcoholic beverages. My earliest memory is of Mother carrying me down the apartment hall naked except for a towel (me, not Mother). She was taking me to the neighbors' for a bath, as our bathtub was being used for some sort of community project which caused Father to fill it with a vile-smelling clear liquid and post "No Smoking" signs all over the place.

Some years later there occurred the events which have since been entered in the minutes of the Rhoades clan as "The Great Beer Bust." The background facts are not entirely clear to me, and Father (hale and hearty though he is at eighty-one) pretends not to recall. I *do* know that several dozen bottles of home-brewed beer were lying on their sides in our attic loft the night of "The Great Beer Bust," and, as luck would have it, the Sisters of the Scripture were meeting in our living room. It was a brutally hot evening in August, and, as I recall, Mrs. Geraldine Gangel was interpreting Ecclesiastes for the ladies, telling them that the preacher meant "selfishness" when he used the word "vanity." This was a typical subject of deep discussion for the Sisters. They would spend hours listening to one of their number tell why "faith, hope, and charity" should be considered to mean "faith, hope, and love."

Listening at the top of the stairs in my pajamas, I would wonder why God hadn't put down "faith, hope, and love" when He whote the Bible, so that Mrs. Geraldine Gangel would not have to interpret for Him, which seemed awfully nervy of her. I was pondering this, in fact, when the first bottle went off. It sounded very much like the Black Tom Explosion.

Mrs. Gangel stopped dead in her explana-

tion. Old Mrs. Bingham, who tended to think of any noises from above as having a supernatural origin, fell heavily to the floor, no doubt on the assumption that Mrs. Gangel had said something *very* wrong. Old Mrs. Bingham quickly scrambled to her feet when Mother explained shakily that it was only the children playing with caps or something.

Immediately another bottle went off, as a sort of exclamation mark on Mother's sentence, and then the bottles began booming in salvos of two and three at a time, seconds apart. The ladies panicked, Father raced out of his study in his bathrobe, Mother took the stairs three at a time to see what was happening, and Charley and I ducked under the covers, a place where children are *absolutely* safe.

What happened then is again murky, but I do know that after the ladies exploded out of the house, they imploded back seeking an explanation and their wraps, and Father met them at the door. It was nothing, he told the ladies; somehow or other a string of leftover cannon crackers from the Fourth had ignited in the attic heat, and heh heh they exploded all over the attic did you ever hear anything so ridiculous in all your life heh heh? Mrs. Arnold W. Hodges inquired as to the chemical composition of the white suds coming out of the attic loft window. That, explained Father, was merely a new type of fire extinguisher he had used just for safety's sake.

This seemed to quiet the ladies, and they wended their individual ways home, even more full of misinformation than when they had arrived. We did not, however, fool our immediate neighbors, whose sense of smell could not long be denied. Father got awful sick and tired of hearing them joke about it for years after. He was especially annoyed with Roger Williams' crack that ours was the only house in the neighborhood with a head on it.

The fact was that Father liked his beer, and if beer was outlawed, he would make it himself. First thing every evening he would enjoy a bottle of cold beer before dinner, a practice which Mother thought barbaric but could not stop. At least, she told Father, he could desist for the sake of the children, who would get the idea that a beer right after work and just before dinner was the natural and moral thing to do. They finally worked out a compromise. Each evening Father would sneak in the back door, and, like a relay racer, grab a cold beer from Mother and run quickly into the broom closet. It took us about three days to catch onto this peculiar habit, but we pretended we didn't know a thing. We would stand behind the back wall of the broom closet and titter over the gurglings and other hydraulic manifestations coming from Father's sanctum. Soon we would hear him leave the closet and tiptoe out the back door, and a few minutes later his heavy footfall would hit the front porch and he would burst inside with a big, "Well, well,

well, how are my nice children tonight?" This went on for years.

We had one other incident involving home-brew, but this time it was root beer that caused all the trouble. Mother used to put it up every summer in dark green bottles with heavy wires drawn over the corks, and then she would let it "rest" in the attic for three or four days. She made one batch with too much yeast or too little yeast (I forget which), and the result was that the root beer fermented slightly. Now if you make this error in brewing root beer, don't expect the children to point out the strange taste later. If something is cold and sweet it meets every requirement of the childish palate, and the fact that a small amount of alcohol—or, for that matter, sulphuric acid—is laced into the drink matters not at all.

Mother served her root beer at a birthday party for my sister Susan, and not only did all the kids drink the foul, beery mixture, but they insisted on seconds. Mother might even have served thirds if she hadn't noticed Chuckie Burcik standing in the corner giggling for no apparent reason. "Chuckie," Mother asked, "whatever in the world is so funny?" Chuckie threw his head back and giggled like a maniac.

And just as Chuckie was inhaling to wind up for another giggle, my brother Charley's voice came clearly across the room. He was telling

Lois Thromkus, "SURE, I'VE SEEN GIRLS' BOTTOMS, AND THEY'RE NOT MUCH TO LOOK AT."

Mother knew now that something was seriously awry, and it didn't take her long to dope it out. She cut off the root beer, locked the doors from the inside, and made a big pot of coffee. An hour or so later, all the kids were permitted to go home, and no one was the wiser. That birthday party, however, became known to its participants as the one by which all subsequent parties were to be measured.

Likewise, a lemonade stand Charley ran also became the standard of excellence in our neighborhood, and for much the same reason. Father had brought home a bottle of vodka, and when

Susan, age five, had asked Mother what it was, Mother quickly answered, "Lemon juice." This was to prove a terrible error of judgment. Little Susan did not forget Mother's words, and a few weeks later, when she was minding Charley's lemonade stand for awhile, she dumped the "lemon juice" into the vat.

It was another hot day, and soon the stand began doing a brisk business, much of it repeats. The bread man quickly sensed that he was onto a good thing. He had five cups and retired to his truck where he was found later, sleeping comfortably atop a tray of Danish. The cop on the beat, Officer Joe David, hovered around the stand for hours, sipping away and exchanging pleasantries with Charley. The mailman remained on our block the whole morning; we had never seen him dawdle so over his deliveries or pass by our house so often. His last comment, before wobbling off to another neighborhood, was addressed to Charley. "I don't know what you put in this lemonade, kid," he said, "but it's the best goddamn lemonade I ever tasted and I mean that in all sincerity."

Charley sold out in half a day—clear profit: sixty-eight cents.

Not long after Charley folded the stand and went inside, Officer Joe David suffered an embarrassing moment. An elderly lady drove past, spotted him, rolled down the window, and shouted, "Come down out of that tree, Officer, you look ridiculous up there!" Officer Joe David tried to explain that it was *cool* in the tree, but he couldn't seem to make her understand.

6

Charley Rhoades, the Animals' Friend

I do not find it easy to talk about my brother Charley. In the first place, he was my *little* brother, which means that I got blamed for acts up to and almost including homicide which were perpetrated by him. And even those activities which were plainly and unmistakably Charley's had a way of catching me up in their backwash, so that even today it is painful for me to think about him. Frequently my wife will awaken me rudely in the middle of the night and say, "Shut up, for God's sake!"

"Huh, huh?" I say. "Whuzzat?"

"You were dreaming about Charley again."

For that matter, I am not the only person so indelibly distorted and emotionally pockmarked by Charley's childhood actions. If you were to rent a sound truck today and ride up and down our old streets intoning, "Charley

Rhoades is back, Charley Rhoades is back," at least a dozen eldering people would dash for cover and pull down their blinds. *That's* how bad it was.

Take, for just a minor example, the matter of the Crawfords' dog. The Crawfords were an odd couple to begin with. Mr. Crawford was a tall, reedy man with a perpetual, glazed grin and a military crew cut. People pointed him out and said he was "shell-shocked." My father said this was odd, as Mr. Crawford had spent the entire war as a supply corporal at Fort Dix, but he supposed Mr. Crawford could have been oversensitive to the goings on at the rifle range. Whatever the whole truth, Mr. Crawford *was* strange. One midnight he was seen running through the woods in his BVD's, laughing and shrieking that the Serbs were pouring through on the right flank. On another occasion he drove his 1929 Hupmobile into a crosswise position on Magnolia Street, thereby blocking all the rush-hour traffic, and demanded to see the *cartes d'identité* of all motorists. "Someone is smuggling Calvados in here," he explained merrily to the policeman, "and the colonel assigned me to the case."

My mother used to tsk-tsk about Mr. Crawford. "The poor thing," she would say. But I never felt sorry for him. He always seemed to be having the time of his life, and so far as I know he still is.

It is a well-known fact that bizarre people tend to have bizarre pets, and the Crawfords were no exception. They had a sheep dog who chased imaginary cars, bayed at the moon even when it was down (pointing to exactly where it had slipped over the horizon), and venerated all living things, especially cats. This dog was insane about children, and the rougher they were on him the more he liked it. His whole rear half used to wag with feverish happiness whenever a child came near; he would emit little yips of delight and roll around in paroxysms of joy. In a word, he was *Mr. Crawford's dog.* There is an order about such things.

My brother Charley was then about six years old and interested in taxidermy, although not quite sure what taxidermy was. I had sent away to one of those "MOUNT BIRDS!" companies which advertised in *The Open Road for Boys,* and Charley had intercepted the kit. It contained everything you needed to mount a squirrel or a trout, but not to mount what Charley had in mind, which was the Crawfords' dog.

As you can see, Charley had no precise ideas about life and death and taxidermy. All he knew was that King was a nice dog and King was there. Charley went to work. First he hacked off some fur, to the accompaniment of little barks of happiness. Then he lacquered the exposed area (a flank and the entire underside), having by now decided to make a front-lawn, life-size statue. Mother entered the garage just as Charley was trying to stuff a handful of cotton batting down the dog's throat, a point at which even King drew the line.

Well, I thought my father was going to go right up in smoke that night. "Never in my life," he kept saying. "Never in my life . . ." King was locked in the garage, half-nude and smelling to the high heavens of lacquer. "What will we do?" Mother asked, wringing her hands. "We can't keep him there forever." Already Mr. Crawford had stalked twice past our house, yelling for King to come on the double.

My father jumped up from the sofa, where he had been sitting with his head in his hands. "Come on!" he said to me, and we headed for the garage. Father opened what was left of the lacquer. "Hold the mutt!" he said. Father re-lacquered the bare spots. I could not understand why Father should want to give King a second coat, but I didn't dare ask. He gathered up the fur snippings lying around and began applying them to the lacquered areas, all the while moaning to himself. An hour later every last strand of fur was back on the dog, though not necessarily in its right place. King did not

look like a dog, but he did not look like anything else, either, and Father had reasonable hopes that Mr. Crawford would take the animal in. We let him out the back door, then raced into our house and turned out the lights, thus giving our place an appearance of blissful innocence.

Father swore us all to secrecy. Charley was threatened with military school for the hundredth time. We were told to stay away from the Crawfords' house, and if we saw them or the dog, to act natural. But nothing dire ever came of it. King was out communing with birds the next day, and Mr. Crawford was to be seen trimming the hedges in their customary fortress-wall design. Within a week all the lacquered-on fur had fallen off, and soon the new fur was growing back. If Mr. Crawford ever suspected anything more than the mange, he never let on.

The trouble with all this was that not enough disaster resulted; Charley did not catch enough hell, and therefore Charley learned nothing from it. So he went from the taxidermy business, which was bad enough, into the veterinary business, which was nearly tragic. His first patient was a male wren. We knew this wren pretty well. For several weeks, he had been busy on our lawn, gathering food for his mate, who was sitting on eggs in the wren house in the back yard. Now somebody had conked this poor little Papa bird with a rock, and Charley brought him into the house for a miracle cure. Mother took one look and said there would be no miracle cure, the bird was dead. Charley laid the pathetic little body on our porch table and went outside to cry in privacy.

That evening Father came into the house and said, "What's that silly wren doing sitting on our front porch?"

We ran out, Charley and I. The bird was sitting up, breathing, but still looking very much on the critical list. "Get a box!" Charley shouted, taking instant command. I got a cigar box and Charley gently lifted the bird inside. "Let's give him a aspirin," the young vet said.

"My God, no," my father said. "You don't give birds aspirin."

"What do you give them?" Charley asked.

"Well," Father said, "a human in that shape, you'd give him some brandy."

The upshot of this was that Charley received permission to spill a couple of drops of rock 'n' rye down the bird's gullet. The wren blinked once, but otherwise failed to react.

"Doubt that he'll make it through the night," Charley said expertly, bedding his patient down on a soft rag in the cigar box.

Charley and I were up simultaneously and racing out to the porch at dawn. The box was empty! From the corner of the room came a tiny "cheeeeeep," and there was the wren, hopping around. Charley laid a flying tackle on him, but the bird squirted straight up in the air and flew nine hundred miles an hour at the window. Crash! The window was closed. The bird fell in a heap of feathers and feet on the cold stone floor.

"Oh," I said. "He's done for now."

"Quick!" said Charley. "Get the whiskey!"

Charley put another half-dozen drops down the bird's beak. Minutes went by. The bird opened one eye. Then the other. He tottered to his feet. Now, like a walking ghost, he slowly stretched his wings and moved.

"Open the door!" Charley hollered. "Open the door!"

Across the floor the wren walked, Charley

steering him with cupped hands. Then—brave little bird—he gave a hippety-hop and took off, flying unsteadily at first, gaining momentum, and finally making his way by a series of chandelles, Immelmanns, and other aerobatic maneuvers to his home.

At once the cheeping of many tiny voices came from inside the wren house. Charley looked at me, and I looked at Charley. A miracle! During the night the eggs had hatched! Oh, lucky Papa Wren, to be home safe and sound with his little family, none the worse for his awful ordeal.

So what do you think Father said when he heard all about this? He said, "You boys think you did that bird a favor, eh? He's gone all night, and his wife has the babies all by herself, and then he comes back home at dawn, and he can barely walk, and he has whiskey on his breath. Some favor you did him."

Mother said that Father was an unfeeling beast, to talk that way about such a beautiful experience, and an awful commotion started. Father said he was only kidding, and Mother said he certainly picked strange things to kid about. Charley and I slank away.

After that there was no stopping Charley. The way he figured it, he had saved that bird's life. "I will devote my life to healing little creatures," he announced. "I have a healing thing in my fingers." When Charley talked like that, trouble was just around the corner.

He set up practice in the garage. There, on a wooden table, he laid out various spoons and forks, a length of dirty rubber hose, some old rags, a leaky pan formerly used to water the cat, a rusty paring knife without a handle, and other instruments of the veterinary profession. His first patients were mice taken in traps about the neighborhood and brought to Charley by the sympathetic children of cruel and heartless parents. Alas, Charley could heal none of them. He would lay them open with the paring knife, but invariably the last spark would already have gone out of the tiny bodies.

These cases were difficult enough for Charley, but there was an added woe: the problem of getting competent help. Charley's nursing assistant was my sister Susan, who was five years old, and she botched up many an operation by handing Charley the wrong instrument. However, Charley reckoned that the experience was valuable for both of them.

We had, at that time, a huge black cat named Tabby, who stood something like sixteen hands tall and weighed a pound or two more than a Bengal tiger. Tabby was three years old, which was a miracle in itself, considering the treatment she got. We used to slide her down the laundry chute, from the second floor to the basement. Charley would put her in the top, and I would stand at the bottom to catch. I will never forget the look of those two hot eyes, glowing like embers, rocketing down the black chute toward me. Tabby would scream with joy—eeeeeoooowwwwrrrrrrrr! ! !—all the way down, and when she landed, her tail would be bushed out like a Christmas tree, and all twenty claws would be extended. I would carry her, yowling and screaming, back upstairs to Charley, and he would try to hold her until I returned to my post. After three or four trips she would tire of the game and squirm out of our grip. Then she would not be seen around our house for several days.

Not long after Charley's miracle cure of the wren, Tabby fell ill, or so it seemed to Charley. He carried her out to the garage, swore Susan to secrecy, and went to work. Deftly probing with skilled diagnostic fingers, Charley soon found out the trouble: Tabby had appendicitis. An immediate operation would be necessary.

They stretched the cat out on her back, and Charley picked up the knife. Tabby twisted and squirmed to the floor. Susan brought her back, but again she got away. Charley decided to wait till the cat took a nap, then to swoop down with his scalpel. But he found that Tabby had a strange inclination to wake up as soon as he began the incision. So he went in the house and commandeered, in the interests of medicine, two items: a tin of sardines and a sleeping pill. He powdered the pill, mixed it with the sardines, and fed it to Tabby. Fifteen minutes later that cat was O-U-T. With Susan holding the cat on its back, Charley went to work.

Mercifully, I find I must draw a curtain over the rest of the scene. Suffice it to say that Susan announced that she was going to be sick, and was, and Charley dug only a small holc in the cat before discovering that he too found the sight of blood less than inspiring, and the whole operation was canceled. Charley told me all about it later, after a Navaho pledge of secrecy, but Susan spilled to Mother, who told Father, and pretty soon the whole family was in a turmoil, and Tabby had been rushed to the vet's—the real vet's—for various antiseptic and corrective procedures.

Charley remained remarkably unperturbed through the whole mess. As he explained to me, he was sorry everybody got so worked up, but what they ought to remember is that every business has its successes and its failures.

7

On the Stream

My father was a fishing nut. He was also a baseball nut, and a driving nut, and a horse-racing nut, and various other kinds of nuts, but mostly he was a fishing nut. Father was at his absolute wildest the night before the opening day of trout season, or, as we called it around our house, "opening night." He would turn the house into a shambles. He would lay out all his tackle on my mother's lace tablecloth in the dining room. I mean *all* his tackle: his bait-casting rig, his six fly rods and assorted fly reels, his boat rod and his surf-casting gear, his waders and his sea boots and his big steel gaff and his vom Hofe reel with the three hundred-yard capacity. Father wasn't fooling anybody. He didn't need one-tenth of that stuff for opening day, but he loved to putter around with it. No amount of reasoning or cajoling by my mother could make him stop. He would lay the whole oily mess on the crocheted tablecloth, and from then until bedtime, Father was in a strange, hypnotic state.

All relatives of trout fishermen are aware of the mesmeric condition which comes on during these sacred rites of "opening night." The symptoms are universal (and they are not, incidentally, exclusive to fishing; some men exhibit the same reactions just before opening a new ship-model kit, or while cooking a steak on the outdoor grill, or while preparing to put a 3/16″ hole in the finger with a new drill press). In Father's case, the first sign was in his eyes. They would glaze over, the pupils would dilate, and from that moment until Father was actually on the stream, he would not blink. He gulped now and then for air, and his cheeks flushed, and his hands shook. But mostly he would bump into things. He would come barreling around the corner looking for Mother's sewing scissors, and he would not quite clear the mantel, and wham! The house would shake. But Father would not shout an obscenity like a lesser man. He would simply race on with his task as though he had felt nothing, and it was the opinion of our family physician that Father *had* felt nothing; Dr. Weiss argued that the opening-day madness in my father brought on a massive release of Novocaine in his system.

I don't know about this, but I do know that my mother walked into the kitchen one opening night and discovered that father was steadying the metal snout of the teakettle with his right hand while steaming flies with his left. "Harvey!" Mother cried. "You'll burn yourself!"

Father snapped his fingers back, released a blood-curdling string of colorful words, and raced for the Unguentine. "God damn it, Caroline," we heard him shout. "Why don't you mind your own business?" It seemed to me that Father was right. If Mother had just kept quiet, Father would never have felt the heat.

In recent years I have interviewed fishing tackle salesmen about this opening-night madness, and I have been pleased to learn that they are all aware of it. They are not perturbed or even confused when a staring, zombielike creature shuffles into the store and orders, as my father did one night, "two ounces of five-pound-test leader and ten yards of ferrule cement." It is old stuff to them, just as it was to my father's clerk. He simply wrapped up two-dozen red worms and bade my father, "Good luck, Harv"; and my father said, "You're quite welcome," and walked out with nothing. I think it was on that opening night, or maybe it was another one, when Father ran two red lights on the way home and pulled up in the driveway just ahead of a siren-screaming police car. Father was calmly heading for the front door when the local law, Dick Leggett, caught up with him.

"Oh, hello, Dick," said Father, his eyes fixed a few inches north-northwest of the constable's hat. "C'mon in. Haven't seen you in awhile."

Two hours later the cop left our house, having been forced to examine (and admire) every reel in the house down to the last pawl. I heard him tell Mother, "Mrs. Rhoades, when Harv's got opening day on his brain, do the whole community a favor, will you? Hide the car keys."

Any evening before a fishing trip found Father at his creative and imaginative best. He was years ahead of his time, and history hasn't yet caught up with him. I read recently a suggestion for getting more distance in bait casting. You simply tie a couple of Alka-Seltzers on your line; this adds weight and distance, and the lozenges melt away in the water, thus reducing the weight of the terminal tackle and enhancing the chances of fooling a fish. Father had this idea twenty-five years ago, only he had it better. Instead of merely putting the lightweight Alka-Seltzer on the line, Father would drill two holes in the wafer. He would attach his line to one hole and a lead sinker to the other, thus using the Alka-Seltzer as a *link* between line and weight. Then Father would be able to cast his worm an unholy distance out in the water, and as soon as it hit, the wafer would bubble away and the lead would drop off, leaving only a hook, a worm, and a line. This, as any good fisherman knows, is exactly what is required to fool canny fish like trout and bass, which will drop a bait instantly if they feel anything unnatural about it.

Father confessed to me that he felt much like Leonardo da Vinci the night he dreamed that one up, and I must say I shared his feelings. We could hardly wait for the next morning and an outing to a small pond in the neighborhood. It was drizzling, but that would not faze two pioneers on the very brink of greatness. We were at the pond forty-five minutes before dawn, after an excruciating hike in which Father bumped into several trees, trampled the azaleas, and almost fell in the Downeys' new well. We had a jarful of predrilled Alka-Seltzers. Look out, bass!

Well, it didn't work that morning. Father opened the Alka-Seltzer jug and began rigging up, but a sudden cloudburst turned the entire bottle into a raging torrent of fizz. Father shouted and raved and stamped his feet. He said that Alka-Seltzer was a lousy product and he would sue, but I calmed him down and explained that the Alka-Seltzer had done exactly what it was supposed to do, and we would try it some other time.

We did, and it is a pleasure to report that the system was a success. Alka-Seltzer has a surprisingly high tensile strength. It resists breaking and chipping, and it carried our night crawlers to the very middle of the ponds, where big fish lay. (In recent years I have experimented with Fizzies and Nervine and other bubbling lozenges, but with little luck. They don't make fishing tackle the way they used to.) Of course, Father had to tie on a new wafer and a new sinker for every cast. But this was a small outlay when one considered the fine strings of bass we brought home.

Was I imagining things, or did those bass

seem to get bigger and stronger as that memorable season wore on? This pond was full of runt bass; they reached full growth at about eight inches, because the food supply was tight. But as July ran into August, and Father carefully pursued his new technique, we began getting occasional ten- and twelve-inchers. One evening Father hooked into a five-inch bullhead that bent his bait rod almost double and made four long runs through the sparkling water before giving up. No, it cannot have been imagination. We *were* getting bigger and better fish. Their color was heightened, they fought with more joie de vivre, and I could swear they came to the net with the trace of a healthy smile around their jaws.

My first trout fishing was on the Waparanic, a little stream that spilled into town from the northeast. My friend Amby Molle went there once with his father, and came racing over to my house that night to tell me about the silvery fish with the long slashes of color down their sides. Up to then, the pinnacle of our fishing careers had been the taking of a six-inch chub in Kearney's Creek on dough bait and thread and No. 16 hooks.

"Aw, c'mon, Amby," I said. "How can they be better than chubs?"

"Chubs," said Amby, "is nothing. N-O-T-I-N-G. Nothing. Only dopes fish for chubs."

So it became a status thing. I had to go to the Waparanic.

Amby and I went early one morning on the bus, both of us loaded to the hairline with tackle on lend-lease from our fathers, who, of course, had not been told of their kindness.

"Don't catch 'em all," the bus driver said, as he let us off in a light rain on Waparanic Road, and it seemed at the time a devilishly clever thing to say.

"Don't catch 'em all," Amby and I repeated, as we giggled our way up the path alongside the creek; already we were consumed by the giddiness and airiness of pre-fishing.

We fished most of the day without a strike. We used flies and spinners and River Runt plugs and Hawaiian Wigglers, and we fished them dead still on the bottom, the proper way, with sinkers. But for some reason, we never had a hit. Then we came to a fence and a sign: "Protected waters. Fly fishing only."

"I know about this stretch," said Amby the Sophisticate. "Fulla trout."

As though to underline his words, we rounded a bend and came upon a pool being beaten to a frazzle by a legion of shiny jumping fish cleaning up on a hatch of flies.

"Holy cow!" I said. "That's the neatest thing I ever saw in my life!"

We tied on new flies and waded in, cheering

and hollering at our good fortune. Amby began whipping his father's fly line over his head and catching leaves, but I was hand-lining mine. You don't get as much distance that way, but you don't catch leaves, either. I whirled the fly line around my head three or four times, like a hammer thrower, and then I winged it far out on the water, six or eight feet away.

"C'mon, baby," I shouted. "Come to Papa!"

Suddenly the trout stopped hitting. This, I have come to learn, is the way with trout. One minute they are smacking everything in sight, and the next minute, inexplicably, they disappear. Amby and I backed out of the pool and trudged sadly upstream. Every now and then we would pass some old guy waving his line back and forth over his head and then laying it out on the water as though it was gold leaf or something. But nobody was catching any trout.

Then we came to another pool where we could see trout finning on the bottom. "Wait!" I said. "I got a neat idea." My idea was that all the junk we had in our tackle boxes and in our pockets was not natural food for trout, but that worms were. "Worms," said Amby, "is not allowed in here. The sign said fly fishing only."

"I know, Amby," I said, full of the fact that my eleventh birthday occurred six months before his, "but my father told me ignorance of the law is no excuse."

Amby seemed satisfied with this explanation, and we withdrew to the bank to overturn rocks and sod for worms. We found plenty.

"Now comes the beauty part of it," I said. I tied on the biggest fly in my father's fly book, and then I slipped a lovely worm on the hook, right over the fly. I plunked the whole thing into the water, and thirty seconds later I had an eight-inch trout flipping on the bank. Those fish, starving for years on feathers and fluff, were finally seeing their first real food.

"Jeez," said Amby, his mouth agape. Soon he had one on, too, and he landed it with a Herculean sporting sweep of his fly rod.

"Wait a minute," Amby said. "Whatta we do if the warden catches us fishing with worms?"

I had already figured that one out. "You seen those guys jerking their lines back and forth over their heads? Well, when the warden comes in sight, you just whip the line till the worm falls off and then you're fly fishing." It was simple.

For the rest of that season, Amby and I were the most successful fly fishermen on the Waparanic. We never failed to fill out our limits. Up until the day disaster struck, we had had only one bad scare. An old guy with a potbelly and $9,000 worth of fishing tackle dangling from his trout vest suddenly materialized out of the brush across the pool, and we knew damned well he had been sitting there watching us for heaven only knew how long. "My, my," I said loudly. "They certainly are hitting today on these dry flies."

"Y-y-y-yeh," said Amby. "They are certainly on the rise today."

We knew that old guy *had* to be a dry-fly purist and he *had* to be a stool pigeon. We let him get out of sight and then we beat it up the path, trailing our lines behind us. All of a sudden Amby stopped and almost knocked me down. "Look!" he said. "Look down there." It was the old guy with the potbelly. He was turning over rocks and dropping things into a rusty can. We went back and fished out our strings.

But on the very next trip we got into bad trouble. It was not Amby's fault and it was not mine. It was some dumb trout's. What happened was this:

We had come prepared with pocketfuls of night crawlers, and we were having a picnic with the way the trout would hit the dangling ends of them but miss the hook. It was great experience in angling finesse. Suddenly I turned to see Amby flailing his line back and forth in the air like a nut, and then I saw the stranger. He had "warden" written all over him. He was wearing a pith helmet and a little gold badge,

and he was standing about fifty feet upstream from us, watching.

"Hi, there, boys," he said.

"Hello," I said, and I gave that old rod a jerk like you have never seen in your life. I was going to snap that night crawler off in one quick, powerful motion. The only trouble was, the line stuck in the water and little rhythmic pulses began shooting down to my hand. I had hooked a trout.

The warden came stumbling over. "Play

him, kid!" he snorted. "Don't horse him now!" I had no intentions of horsing him. I intended to play him for three days if necessary. I intended to play him until the warden had to go home for dinner, at the very least. But the warden had different ideas. "All right, kid," he said after a few minutes. "You got him licked now. Bring him in."

I gathered the line in inch by inch, reciting to myself the Nicene Creed, which was all that popped into my head at the moment. And then the trout was lying spent at my feet. I had foul-hooked him just ahead of the tail, and there was an inch of night crawler hanging from the fly.

"Holy mackerel!" I said. "He's been feeding on worms."

The warden knelt down and took a good look. "Yeh," he said slowly. "But he's been feeding at the wrong end."

"Strangest thing I ever saw," I said. Out of the corner of my eye I could see Amby inching away. I hoped that he, at least, would make a getaway, so that my parents, in long years to come, would know where I was.

"Stand still, kid!" the warden cried, suddenly ripping off his mask of kindness and understanding. "What chew got in those pockets?" He frisked us as though we were common criminals, and dropped the contraband at our feet: a stack of wriggling night crawlers. You'd have thought it was heroin or cigarettes. "Now I invite you boys the hell outa here!" he said. "Get home as fast as your scurvy little legs can carry you, and if I ever see you around here again I'll run you in."

That was our last trip to the Waparanic. I have not ever been back, and neither, I'm sure, has Amby. The fly-fishing stretch may still be there, and if it is, I can heartily recommend it to you. But watch out. The warden is a narrow-minded crumb, and you had better see him before he sees you.

8

You Can't Fool Old Doc Trask

WHEN you're a kid, you wonder how adults can be so stupid. When you grow up, you realize that maybe they hadn't been so stupid after all; maybe they knew all along what you were up to. Take old Doc Trask, the druggist. For years he had been selling pipe tobacco to me and Charley for our father—pipe tobacco and no other kind of tobacco. Then all of a sudden up pops Charley, aged twelve, fingers trembling, counting out fourteen pennies on Doc Trask's counter, and saying in a wobbly voice, "One pack of Sir Walter Riley cigarettes, please, for my father. They're for my father."

"I thought your father only smoked a pipe, Charley," said old Doc Trask.

"No doubt about it, Doc," said Charley, "unless they can beat the Yankees four straight." Who will ever know what Charley thought Doc had asked, and what Charley's answer meant? When a fellow is pulling off his first big job, he can't be blamed for becoming a little nervous. Doc gave him the Raleighs, and Charley went out and smoked himself sick, and no one was the loser.

When I look back, there were hundreds of pranks and tricks and cons we pulled, thinking that we were so clever that nobody knew, but now I wonder if we ever did anything that wasn't detected. We used to call up Doc Trask every now and then and say, "Is this the Trask Pharmacy on Heilman Road?" He would say, "Yes," and we would say, "Well, you better get off, there's a car coming." Or we would say, "Do you have Prince Albert in the can?" He would say, "Yes," and we would say, "Well, you better let him out, he's suffocating." All kinds of brilliant, avant-garde jokes.

One night my father took me into the Trask Pharmacy and asked for a tin of Edgeworth pipe tobacco. "Yes, sir, Mr. Rhoades," said Doc Trask. "I've got Edgeworth"—he turned and looked me straight in the eye—"and I've also got *Prince Albert in the can.*" I got his message.

If I had to name the three most important places in my childhood, Doc's would have to be one of them. It was where I first stole. It was where I spent my first allowance of a nickel a week on Tastykakes. It was where I took my first dates for a big-deal Coke after the big-deal movies. Doc's was one of the early prototypes

of those giant drug stores that now will sell you everything from a gumdrop to the *Berengaria*, except that Doc handled it all himself: the candy counter, drug section, soda fountain, airplane-and-ship model section, toy department, magazine stand, and photo booth. He also had a pay phone which we used to flush. You flush a pay phone by putting in a nickel and then quickly hanging up. Your nickel is returned and every now and then a whole collection of coins comes out along with it. I'm not sure of the mechanics of this, but Doc told me once that the operator has a "collect" button on her switchboard; when you put your money into the pay slot, it doesn't fall down into the cash-box until the operator pushes the "collect" button. But sometimes she forgets to push the button and collect the money; it stays up in the top of the phone box, and the first person to "flush" the phone collects everything. What an exciting game, and what good odds! You always got your nickel back, at the very least, and if the previous phoner had been calling long distance, you could haul in a buck or two. I'll bet you *still* could.

Doc also had a pinball machine, and I will have to admit right here and now that pinball machines were my real sin as a kid. I used to drop everything—homework, chores, cornet lessons, trysts with girls—to race down to Doc's and listen to the jangle and whirrrrrrrr and the clunk-bang-zing-crash-ding-ding-ding-ding of that machine. When we got a little older and had some cash on hand, we used to meet at Doc's after school and try to "run up" some free games quickly and cheaply. In no time we would have twenty or thirty free games registered, and then it would be every player's task to keep the level high, so we could play free for the rest of the afternoon. Occasionally we were helped by a long wire which we would thrust through the crack under the glass and shove repeatedly against a bumper, thus sending the score up into the millions while the free-game indicator kept spinning merrily. This dodge might have worked forever if it hadn't been for Edward Brawley, the worst "bragger" in the neighborhood. One day we ran up ninety-seven free games by using the wire, and Edward couldn't resist calling Doc over and saying, "How do you like that, Doc? Pretty good shooting, eh?" Doc was a friendly guy, and he wasn't trying to get rich off his pinball machines, and so he smiled and walked up to the machine and studied the colored lights and the long lines of numbers shining brightly and the tiny light of the free-game indicator. Then he turned to Edward and Amby Molle and me and he said, "I don't know what you boys are doing, but don't do it any more. Play the game fair and square." Three innocent faces looked at him, and big-mouth Edward said, "Oh, we did do it with skill, Doc. Scout's honor." Doc said over his shoulder as he walked away, "How did you do it with skill when you ain't even shot your first ball yet?" Sure enough, the ball tray at the bottom of the machine was empty.

That incident more or less forced us to rely on skill from then on, and even though I say so myself (and my grandmother used to say, "Self-praise stinks!"), we became the hottest athletes you ever saw on pinball. (This is no idle boast, but a matter of record: In 1947 I won the pinball championship of the University of Pennsylvania, in 1948 Amby was champ at Duke, and Edward Brawley went on to become champion of the Greater South Philadelphia Boy's Clubs in 1950, all because of our training in fundamentals at Doc Trask's.) We were the absolute masters of "jostling" (pronounced "joz-zell-ing"), the technique by which the steel ball is made to gyrate around the table according to its master's wishes, and with complete contempt for the awful sign:

TILT

My technique was the best (I am throwing all modesty to the winds now), because it was based on the rhythm and "feel" and flow of the game. I would grasp the machine about halfway up on its sides, and without releasing my grip give it the old "English" gently from side to side and up and down, at *precisely* the right instant. Amby and Edward used the more flashy "pounding" technique or the "palm jostle," where you rap the machine with the heels of your hands. A player skilled in this technique will let the ball work its way down the table, registering its score en route, and then, just before it reaches the ball tray at bottom, he times its fall against a bumper, and WHACK! He smacks the machine just as the ball hits, and back it goes to the very top of the machine to begin the scoring descent once again. The only trouble with this technique is that it gives the player too little real control; he can make the ball move fast, but he can't direct its path any too well. With my less bombastic system I could keep that ball bouncing on the same scoring bumper for a half-hour, playing "Yankee Doodle" at the same time. Crowds of other boys would gather to watch; boys I liked, boys I disliked, boys who had beaten me up or stolen girls from me, all sorts of boys, and I was the absolute *king* around that pinball machine, and there was no argument about it. I suppose everybody has some achievement like that in his early life, something he can chew over and remember with pride, while his wife is saying, "Whatever in the world are you smiling about?"

I went back to Doc Trask's for the first time in ten years, and it was hardly changed, except that now there were two pinball machines instead of one. A group of young teen-agers was congregated around, and wheels were turning and lights were flashing and bells were ringing. I watched a chubby kid use a palm jostle to work the ball up and down a scoring channel, but he lost control after three round trips and the ball dropped into the tray at the bottom. I couldn't help observing to myself that the kid had shown rotten form, but he was young, and it was still too early to give up on him.

9

Words, Words, Words

I was almost in my teens before I learned that the big hero of my childhood was not called Sir Lank-a-lot. I used to admire Sir Lank-a-lot because he would go out and risk his life for his fiery princess. He battled giant ogres, which I pronounced "orgs," and he was kind and fair to the bed-raggled underdog, even to the village eye-dot. One thing about Sir Lank-a-lot: He had plenty of red corp-suckles. And he and his whole corpse of men stuck together through all sorts of misshapes; they were untied to the end.

By the time I was ten I had a galloping vocabulary of words I had never heard spoken, but had read often and mispronounced entirely on my own. They would cascade through my mind, and it would be a thrill to see one pop up, like an old friend, in the newspapers. "Everything is going orry in the business world," I would read to myself. Or:

"The mole-ster broke into the house through a window."
"The president said it was a real threat to be home again."
"Jemore Adams, the victim, said he was my-zelled by the honest face of the swindler."

(I am not entirely straight even today on "awry," "Jerome," and "misled," but I figure I'm one jump ahead of a classmate who persists in pronouncing "gauge," "mortgage," and "Risë Stevens" exactly as they are spelled.)

One of our favorite works was *Alsop's Fables,* and we especially appreciated the fact that each fable had a morale. Buck Rogers was flying high in those days, and he had at least one small fan in our neighborhood who referred to small planets as hemorrhoids. I suppose he had heard the word around his house, and mixed it up with asteroids or something. Nobody ever seemed offended about it, except my mother.

Words were just words, unfreighted little wisps of sound. You wrote down certain symbols to express certain sounds, and why get excited about it? Thus, I wrote for my second-grade teacher my favorite lines of poetry:

I wanna live ina house by the side of the rode
And be a fiend to man.

It was in the middle of the third grade when a great awakening came upon all of us. Our teacher read the rolling, throbbing lines of a great new American poet, and we were all moved to deep, childlike admiration. Caught up in the sweep of his lyric grandeur, I wrote the lines in my notebook:

> It takes a heepa livin
> To make a house a hoam.

Underneath, I inscribed the poet's name: "Ed Gray Guest."

Bad as I was, my brother Charley was the neighborhood's worst menace when it came to words and sounds. He repeated everything he heard, usually at precisely the wrong time. And he was totally devoid of taste. My mother choked on her food and my father's face turned ashen when Charley announced at a family reunion Thanksgiving dinner: "A funny man came to the door yesterday and he ast me was my mother home and I tole him yes she was sittin' on the toilet."

And one day we were out for a drive in the country and we passed a bull and a cow mating and that fool Charley wouldn't let the subject drop. "Boy!" he kept saying. "Did you see that! Boy, what neat tricks those cows was doing!"

My father always figured that Charley's lubricous tendencies developed quite innocently from an experience of early childhood. It was World Series time, and who should wander into the neighborhood bar but Charley, aged five. Normally, this was a quiet little spa where traveling salesmen and cops would drop in for a beer and peanuts. But now, with the Series blaring out of the radio, the bar was jammed with all sorts of people, including some construction workers with rich and variegated lexicon.

It developed later that Charley had stood unnoticed in the corner of the bar for quite some time before Mr. Irving, the owner, suggested that he go home. That night, at the dinner table, my mother told Charley to eat his cauliflower. I cannot, even now, bring myself to report exactly what Charley answered, but in essence he suggested to my mother that she take the cauliflower and perform a bizarre biological feat with it. I will never forget the expression on my father's face when Charley added the word "sideways."

Mother and Father worked patiently to purge Charley of his collection of colorful new words and phrases, and after a month they permitted him to return to Sunday School. But the mind is a wondrous thing, and the five-year-old Charley had filed away in some dusty curlicue of his brain one choicely misheard phrase which was not to be used by him for half a decade.

It came out when Charley was in the seventh grade. He had made a pair of book ends in woodshop. The day he brought them home, all clear-shellacked and piny smelling, my mother's Bible study group was assembled at our house, and the members were engaged in their customary practice of gobbling hors d'oeuvres, gossiping about the pastor, and (once in a great while) reading the Bible. In walked Charley with his treasure. "Why, Charles," my mother said. "What a perfectly lovely piece of work." The other ladies started gurgling and cooing, and Charley was embarrassed. Modesty welled up within him, and all the ladies heard him say sweetly, "It's just a half-assed job."

The ladies left shortly afterward, and Mother put in a rush call to Father at his office. He came straight home and banished Charley to his room under orders to write the offending expression one thousand times. "Maybe that'll clean up your foul tongue!" Father shouted.

Three hours later a puzzled Charley brought his work down for inspection. He had done a neat job. Scrawled across a stack of yellow papers, row on row on row, were the words: "Half-fast, half-fast, half-fast. . . ."

10

Charley and the Human Form Divine

CHARLEY was a little kid for his age, and he was always treated like the baby of the family, and so he was totally unprepared for the boy's locker room routine when he entered junior high school at the age of eleven. Now this may come as a surprise to some, but the idea of a sweaty, steamy commune where boys run in and out of the shower all stark buff buck nude naked takes some getting used to. Boys have modesty, too, especially boys in whose families the human form has been treated as a rather scandalous secret which must not be let out.

I remember my own first day in the boy's locker room. We were outfitted with gym suits, sneakers, and the other equipment, assigned combination locks, and steered to our very own lockers. The only trouble was that somebody else's very own locker was right next door, and there we were: thirty kids lined up in a long row, looking sheepishly at one another. By now there was no doubt in anybody's mind: we were supposed to take off our clothes and put on the gym suits, RIGHT IN FRONT OF EVERYBODY ELSE! One kid, Bobby Werner, requested permission to go upstairs to the office and call his mother. That was the last we saw of Bobby Werner. He was transferred to a private school, Chadwick, where (we were certain) every kid had a plush private dressing room of his own.

We finally all got dressed, owing to the fine example set by three or four boys from "down the woods" where there was an old swimming hole ("Brass Beach," they called it, in an admirable contraction). These boys yanked their clothes off as though it was nothing and pretty soon were slapping one another's bare backsides with towels, and in this slight diversionary activity the rest of us slid out of our knickers and our underwear, and by dint of clever crisscrossing of the hands succeeded in dressing without giving too much away.

Imagine our consternation when we learned, after the gym hour was over, that we were expected to strip again and race merrily through a U-shaped shower area before redressing, and that Mr. Johnston, the teacher, was going to stand there to check on it. Imagine! Mr. Johnston! Why, he wasn't even our father.

Tom Comlin went all the way through the

U in a sort of sideways shuffle, no doubt on the theory that this would expose only his bare bottom to Mr. Johnston's view, keeping the rest a private matter. A few of the boys went through carrying towels, which they fluttered nonchalantly in front of them as though it were a perfectly normal thing to go through a shower carrying a towel. My own technique was to run through the forty or fifty feet of U at such a tremendous rate of speed that anybody observing me would see only a blur. I brought this off fairly well, except that Amos Harris passed me and almost tripped me en route.

After a few weeks, of course, all this silly shame was forgotten and it became a problem to get us *out* of the shower. Indeed, we reveled in standing around naked and manly and glittering with water. I will leave the explanation of all this to Dr. Freud, since it is unclear to me.

Charley—as I started to say—didn't show up at gym class until the rest of his classmates had gone through the shakedown period and had grown accustomed to one another's nude splendor. The reason Charley was late was because he had to have his tonsils and adenoids out the very day school opened, and he was excused from gym for two weeks. It wouldn't have been that long, except that the doctor noticed, when examining Charley, that he had not been circumcised, and suggested to our parents that this minor detail be attended to while Charley was already under the ether. This sounded practical to all concerned. When Charley woke up after the surgery, Mother and our minister, Mr. Sidingham, were at his bedside clucking and gooing and bearing gifts.

"How do you feel, sweetheart?" Mother gushed.

"My tonsils feel okay," Charley croaked, "but"—he reached toward his abdomen—"it sure hurts where they took out my adenoids."

So this was why Charley didn't go to gym class for two weeks, and why Fred Subar and Harold Dunne had their chance to work up their prank on him. They were all assigned to the same corner of the locker room. Charley showed up bearing the usual newcomer's stack of clothes: sneakers, shorts, shirt, socks, and a little cardboard box bearing a protective male undergarment. One by one Charley put the items on, but when he was fully dressed the protective male undergarment was left over. "Hey," said Charley. "What's this?"

"That," chorused Fred and Harold, "is a nose guard."

"No kiddin'?" Charley asked.

"No kiddin'," said Harold. "If they gave you one, that means the school nurse says you gotta wear it."

It fit perfectly. Charley told me later that it was kind of exciting to be wearing a nose guard just like a professional athlete. Up the metal stairs to the gym he climbed, and burst into the view of thirty expectant kids.

Now the idea had been to let Charley go on in ignorance until Mr. Johnston came out of his little caged office to call the class to order. But a few weak ones couldn't keep from laughing, and that set them all off.

Charley, shocked and confused, turned to run back into the dressing room, but in his panic he got mixed up and went out the wrong door, winding up in the hall. Miss Van der Schmidt caught sight of him from her classroom and came bursting out the door followed by two of her girl students. "Stop!" she shouted. "Where do you think you're going?"

Charley explained he was going to the locker room, but he had made a wrong turn.

"What in the world is that on your face?" one of the girls asked.

"It's a nose guard," Charley said. His voice was slightly muffled.

"A what?" the other girl said.

Miss Van der Schmidt quickly got between Charley and the girls and blurted out, "It's a nose guard!" in a high-pitched, semi-hysterical voice.

Charley finally was propelled back into the gym where Mr. Johnston patiently explained the equipment, and Charley retired to the dressing room to put everything in its proper place.

That afternoon my mother had a call from the principal, but he said he would call back later, that it was *Mr.* Rhoades he wanted to talk to. But I don't think he ever pursued the matter any further, and the only after effect was that every kid in the school had something to kid Charley about now. For months and months he was twitted with that hoary baseball question, "Say, are you a Phillies' rooter or an Athletic supporter?"

Charley finally learned to answer, "I don't know. Go ask your sister."

That quieted them. Nobody could stay one up on Charley for long.

daughter whose first word was
age of two and was exactly four
nd in the perfect tradition of
ength. Gwil knew what it meant,
Marilyn, didn't, and they found
the peculiar position of having
al discussion about their infant's

a child, the mention of such
l would have caused his parents
ce or at the very least to send
ary school. Just to give you an
gh it was:
twelve, I had a pretty good
n, chipped from nearby quar-
Hoween abandoned during the
y I found a yellowish-white
n the face of a cliff, and my
, told me it was saltpeter.
n at sor and asked my father what
ms likeie of your business!" father
l corsetsng me feel like Bluebeard
y enough Nelson at the least. That
sinister s mby and me probe into
ait to pick e encyclopedia and visit
n was avail everything else, but the
ine was that saltpeter was
ldren om doing something that
s, andding young boys would
My c

My little s
prematurely
apparel. On
Burton, wa
Gardiner's
a brassière,
as though
who was m
"Someth
Susan a
vance, and
would wr
down. Sus
"A BRA
a piece of
"Oh,"
kids?"
"Eight
"Nine
They
There
porters
about w
us that
hood, a
formati
Sears, I
Now
these t
ents w

Rhoades has
spoken at the
letters long a
words of that l
but his wife,
themselves in
a long semantic
first word.

When I was
a word by a kid
to call the poli
him off to milit
idea of how rou

When I was
mineral collectio
ries which had b
depression. One da
substance growing o
buddy, Amby Molle
I took a piece home
it was used for. "Nor
said with heat, maki
the Pirate or Babyface
reaction only made A
the dictionary and th
the public library and
best we could determ
used to keep you fr
we two fine upstan
never do anyway.

Another time I asked Father what bur-les-que meant, and he said it was a kind of entertainment "you wouldn't want to see." When I pressed for further details, he rolled his eyes wildly and looked panicky at my mother and ran to the bathroom, saying over his shoulder, "You really wouldn't care to know." That's what *he* thought. Now I was positive that bur-les-que must be something absolutely sensational, a fact which I was not able to confirm until I was sixteen.

11

The Hatred of Uncle Harry

MY great-uncle, Harry Rhoades, was a fanatic and a liar and my favorite distant relative. He was my favorite because he was extremely entertaining and because he didn't have the vaguest idea he was a fanatic and a liar. He simply thought that he was years ahead of his time and honest to a fault. It was the system that was wrong and dishonest.

He was my father's uncle, and therefore he possessed the Rhoades family's remarkable ability to get every story, every theory, every concept just *a little wrong*. I well remember, as an example, Uncle Harry's discussion of the birth rates of monkeys. "Monkeys is so reproductive," he told my brother Charley, my mother, and me, "that it is a phenomena. Monkeys have six or eight babies every half a year, and soon the babies start having babies. It is a scientific fact that if you put two monkeys in a room and let them reproduce, sooner or later *they would write Hamlet!*"

Charley and I sat gape-mouthed in wonderment, but Mother said, "I wouldn't be surprised," and went right on knitting. She had spent a lifetime listening to ideas like this, and nothing was going to faze her now.

Uncle Harry had moved in with us during the mid-thirties, and he stayed on for two years until he found work. At first, we kids had no idea why a full-grown and apparently healthy man should be out of a job. For that matter, we had no idea what line of work he was in, nor would he enlighten us. One day I asked him point-blank what he did, and he said he was a flautist by trade. I asked him what a flautist was, and he said it was a man who played the flaut. "I used to play flageolet," he added, "but I quit because I always lost." You can see how enlightening this was, and I got the idea (correctly, as it turned out) that Uncle Harry didn't want to discuss his line of work.

One other thing that puzzled us about Uncle Harry was the pile of bricks he kept just inside our vestibule. Whenever one of the electric company's trucks would go by our house, Uncle Harry would pick up a brick and give chase. Down the street he would sprint, whooping like a wild Indian. Most often, the truck would get away, but every now and then Uncle Harry

would score with a beautiful lob right through a window. Then he would rub his hands together and run excitedly back to the house, trembling all over, saying to anyone who would listen, "That'll bitch the sons of fixes."

Something else Uncle Harry liked to do was tree the phone company's linesmen. He would trail their green trucks for miles until they would stop and set up their little tents in the air, repairing some defect in a line. Then he would begin pelting them with rocks and obscenities. "Come on out and fight, you dirty obscenities!" he would shout, and when one of the linemen would poke his head out of the tent, Uncle Harry would let fly with diabolical accuracy. Many an SOS was tapped into the phone company's lines that summer.

Such things could not continue without some sort of explanation to us kids, and finally, after much prodding, Mother provided one. Uncle

Harry, she explained, bore the electric company a terrible grudge (he had nothing whatever against the telephone company, except that he felt certain they had some connection with the electric company, which was just another of those things he kept getting *a little wrong*). For twenty years Uncle Harry had worked as a meter reader. When the depression began to tighten belts, Uncle Harry came up with a typical example of Rhoades fuzzy-think, as follows:

1. The electric company is a public utility, owned by the public.
2. The people in this neighborhood *are* the public, and they don't have enough money.
3. Therefore I will read their meters low.
4. Nobody will be getting cheated because the electric company is owned by these same people in this neighborhood.

The logical defects in these propositions were not immediately apparent to Uncle Harry, and so he read the meters low for five years. It is my opinion even today that far more good than harm came out of Uncle Harry's practice. The people had a little more money for food. The electric company was able to use Uncle Harry's route in an advertisement pointing out that "electricity is cheaper than ever," which it certainly was in that area. On one occasion average bills from Uncle Harry's territory were presented by the electric company to the state public utilities commission as part of an argument for a rate increase, which was granted. Uncle Harry, for his part, enjoyed the respect and admiration of the people on his route ("my clientele," he used to call them). They didn't know what he was doing, but they did know that their electric bills had been most reasonable during his regime.

The trouble with such a plan is that it must eventually be found out. "Eventually" may be ten years or twenty years or fifty years. But the very nature of the meter-reading system makes it impossible to cheat over the long pull. Let us say Uncle Harry reads your meter one month and it says 10,000. He tells the company that your reading is only 9,990, and you get billed for 10 less units than you actually used. But what can Uncle Harry do the following month? Now your meter reads 10,500. If he turns in the accurate figure, you are going to get stuck for the 10 units he shaved off last month. If he deducts 10 units again and turns in a figure of 10,490, he has done you no favor this month. You will pay for 500 units, and you have used 500 units. So in order to keep the thing going, Uncle Harry had to make deductions on top of deductions, and keep a whole extra set of books showing what he had turned in last month, what the original figure had been, etc., etc.

As a typical Rhoades, Uncle Harry refused to admit to himself that he was in over his mathematical head. With bulldog tenacity he would sit in his furnished room at night for three and four hours at a stretch, going over his multiple-entry books. One afternoon, groggy from lack of sleep, Uncle Harry forgot himself and turned in an accurate reading for the Bollwegs' house on Walnut Street. The Bollwegs got an electric bill of $438 for the month, and there was hell to pay. A supervisor went over every inch of Uncle Harry's territory and found tens of thousands of kilowatt-hours flying around unaccounted for.

Uncle Harry was called in and confronted with the facts. "The electric company is a public utility," Uncle Harry began, "and these people are the public. . . ."

Uncle Harry was fired. There would have been criminal charges, too, except that the company executives remembered all too clearly that a whole advertising campaign and a successful rate case had been based on Uncle Harry's activities.

As for the dangerous criminal himself, he shouted that the entire affair was another case of "the public be damned," and he vowed to "get" the whole electric company before he was finished. There was no denying the basic strength of his position. Uncle Harry had lost a job, but he had gained a lifelong license to cannonade the electric company's rolling stock with impunity. A lot of people would make the same trade.

Through his two years with us, Uncle Harry never lost this zest for chasing the trucks, but toward the end we noticed that the quarry seemed to appear less often. One day an old buddy from the electric company called on Uncle Harry and told him that the company had mapped out a series of alternate routes; they were by-passing us.

"Those bastards!" Uncle Harry cried. "They'll stop at nothing!" Thereafter he took to lurking around street corners and in vacant lots in different parts of town, his stack of bricks at the ready. But by and large this was unproductive.

One day he found a job as night clerk in a small hotel, and this provided all Uncle Harry asked of life: room and board and a good, clear view of passing traffic. One summer night in 1939 Uncle Harry died on the street, the victim of a heart attack at the very height of the chase. It was exactly how he would have wanted to go: with a brick in his hand and the wind on his face, battling for truth and right.

Father inadvertently pronounced the eulogy

a few weeks after the funeral. Trying to explain Uncle Harry to a friend, Father said, "Harry needed a little hatred. It gave direction to his life."

12

How to Make Money though Young

When I was a child money was where you found it or conned it or made it or stole it. Nowadays, by and large, kids get allowances; these are supposed to teach them how to budget, how to live within an income, how to save, etc. It has been my unfortunate experience with my own kids that they learn no such things. They merely do not learn how to find money or con it or make it or steal it. They only learn how to accept it, which is of little use in later life.

Oh yes, we got allowances, but you could stick them in your ear, they were so small. I got a nickel a week along with a boring admonition from Father, "Heh, heh, don't spend it all in one place, heh, heh."

Usually I would get my allowance Sunday night, and I would pitch and toss for hours trying to decide what to do with it the next day. Come Monday I would embark on a riotous orgy of spending. One week I would buy a Catherine wheel, which would sometimes last for as long as two or three hours before all the emery would be gone. Or I would get a whistle or a mittful of licorice or a water pistol or a grab bag or bubble gum cards. But most often I would buy a package of Tastykakes, which cost a nickel but which were just about the only five-cent investment containing enough sugar to satisfy a little kid's sweet tooth.

The sweet tooth is a phenomenon which fully illustrates the perversity of time and life. To put the matter in simple form, I have reduced it to what I call Rhoadcs' Law:

> There is nothing in the world a human being wants more than sweets until he can have all the sweets he wants and then there is nothing in the world he wants less.

The irony of this is that half the world—*i.e.*, the kids—goes around with its collective tongue hanging out for sweets and can't afford them, and the other half goes around with thc wherewithal but not the craving. Imagine how much more orderly life would be if it were the adults who had the craving and the kids who didn't. Wall Street bankers could go out and have a dozen hot fudge sundaes for lunch, and kids could look in bakery windows without suffering Oriental agonies.

It is my own opinion that far too little scientific attention has been paid to the role of the sweet tooth in modern society. Dr. Freud talks about unfulfilled desires and the terrible frustrations of childhood, and never mentions the number-one frustration of all time: The frustration of wanting a Hershey bar and not having a nickel. The reason Dr. Freud ignored this (aside from the fact that there were no Hershey bars in Vienna) is that he wrote as an adult, and the adult, according to Rhoades' Law, has lost his interest in Hershey bars.

What *does* the adult care about? *You* know. And so did Dr. Freud, and so that's what he wrote about. If children wrote books explaining adults, there would be far more emphasis on significant things like candy and far less on s-x.

All around us is evidence of the power and importance of the drive-to-sweets. Living in my house, for example, is a two-year-old boy who will claw your eyes out if you get between him and an M&M's ("melts in your mouth, not in your hand"). There is a five-year-old girl who stacks up three chairs and climbs them like a human fly to get at a forbidden box of cube sugar. There is a twelve-year-old boy who once ignored a fever of 103, chills, vomiting, diarrhea, and double vision to stumble into the living room because he overheard his mother say, "Oh, Harry, hello." He thought she had said, "Oh, cherry Jello!"

I happen to know that more than one of the juvenile murders in recent years was caused by fights over sweets. I have seen kids—Charley and me, to name only two—who were willing to lie and cheat and steal just to get sweets. Would we have lied and cheated and stolen to beat out our father for our mother's love? Maybe, but not if there had been any candy around to lie and cheat and steal about. *That's* how much Dr. Freud knew.

We used to have all kinds of action going in order to satisfy this primordial craving. One technique was simply to pass the old hand across the old candy counter and come up with a Baby Ruth or some other wonder of the world. Personally I found this technique unworthy of us. It had no finesse, and if you were caught, you were dead, finished, kaput. Our local merchants didn't catch many kids, but when they did, the kids were barred forever, a punishment far too painful to [illegible].

A better technique was worked up by me, and you will excuse me if I refer to it as "The Great Hershey Bar with Almonds Swindle." I still burst with pride when I consider that all the details were worked out when I was a mere eight years old.

The A&P, in those days, had a single-cashier system. You went into their grocery section and you ordered everything you wanted, and the grocer gave you a little bill showing how much you owed. Then maybe you went to the meat section and the butcher gave you another bill. You paid all the bills as you left.

I would go to the A&P for my mother, get bills from the grocer and the butcher, and then begin my dramatic performance. I would snap my fingers, say loudly, "Oh, I forgot something," then pick up a Hershey bar with almonds and hand it ostentatiously to the grocer. (Don't ask me why it was always Hershey bars with almonds; they just happened to be my big craze then, and I would have fought "Bronko" Nagurski or Jim Londos or a whole herd of King Kongs for one.) The grocer would make up an extra bill reading "$0.05," put the Hershey bar in my sack, and send me merrily on my way. I would pay the grocery and meat bills, but not the Hershey bar with almonds bill, and nobody would be the wiser.

I worked this dodge weekly for two years until we moved to a neighborhood where there was no A&P, which was a good thing, because if we had kept living near an A&P things might be different now for Huntington Hartford.

I am especially proud of my A&P technique because it is one of the few bona-fide individual systems worked up by any of us kids. The rest of our rackets depended upon "confederates," a word which we learned from our juvenile books ("nearby lurked a confederate, ready to do the villainous Snark's evil bidding").

One of the simplest two-man systems was for one kid to ask the grocer if he had any wooden boxes to give away. (*All* little boys want *all* wooden boxes at *all* times.) Invariably, the grocer would take the culprit into the back of the store and show him a cluttered area and suggest that he look around for himself. Meanwhile, the confederate would dip into the candy counter and slink away. Sometimes it would be a double dip, but never more. I will have to give us credit: We never stole more than two candy bars at a time, and usually we took just one. The reason was that Sammy Firestone's father was a lawyer and that made Sammy our legal advisor, and Sammy explained that taking one or two candy bars was a misdemeanor but taking more than two was a felony and then you were in *real* trouble. Sammy also told us one day that the statue of limitations on stealing candy bars was one year and that we could go into Doc Trask's drug store and brag to him about taking candy last year and there was nothing Doc could do about it. I pointed out that there was no statue of limitations on what Doc could tell our parents. If there was one thing Sammy Firestone proved, it was that a little learning can be disastrous.

When I was ten or eleven, Father doubled my allowance. I suppose he thought this would change my entire standard of living and solve all my monetary problems, but the truth was that I now looked on this piddling Sunday-evening handout as a mere joke. What was a nickel or a dime to me, the Baron Rothschild of Knauth Avenue? I had activities going which would have made the Securities and Exchange Commission, the Federal Trade people, and the FBI send battalions of agents into town, if they had only known.

Charley, too, had grafts and cons, which he tried to keep from me. But I managed to find out about most of them. Afer all, I had eyes, and I was a kid. Charley could tell my parents that he *found* that dollar bill and they would believe him, but I would know that Bobby Werner had got a dollar bill for his birthday and that Bobby and Charley had been having a long talk about Charley's new aggie that very morning. The whole set of circumstances would read like a book to me, and I would not be at all surprised the next day when Charley would turn up with the dollar bill *and* the new aggie.

But that was Charley's business. He had his side of the street and I had mine. Mostly I was concerned with taking adults. In the first place they had more to give. And they were such patsies. Let us consider, for a starter, the snow-shoveling technique for relieving adults of their money.

When I was a kid, we could pick up twenty-five or thirty cents for doing the average suburban snow-shoveling job. (Nowadays you would have to give a kid nine thousand dollars and two hundred shares of U.S. Steel pfd. to do the same amount of snow-shoveling, *if* he would do it at all.) We would get this crummy twenty-five or thirty cents for about two hours' hard work, and every penny would be well earned.

It didn't take me long to learn how to turn a bigger profit in the snow-shoveling profession. I would get an okay from the customer to go ahead with the job. I would take longer than necessary with her walks. I would make a big production out of scraping and banging at non-existent patches of ice. Finally I would turn up at the front door, huffing and puffing from my exertions, and announce that I was finished. The lady of the house would ask, "How much do I owe you, little boy?" Near collapse from overwork, I would barely manage to gasp, "Fifteen cents."

Some of the ladies would chuckle and pat

me on the head. Some would turn and brush away a tear. Some would invite me in for cookies and hot chocolate. But *all* would refuse to pay me any such silly sum as fifteen cents. They would go digging in their purses and come up with pirates' treasures like fifty-cent pieces and, more than once, dollar bills.

My finest hour came at the home of Mrs. Trillingham Walsh, who was getting on in years. It took me three hours of work and histrionics to do her place. It should have taken only about an hour, but now and then I would see her, out of the corner of my eye, watching me from a window. For such a good audience, a fellow likes to put out his best. At one point I was even on my knees, scraping away with a fingernail at what purported to be a stubborn fleck of ice. Finally I dragged myself to her front door and told her she owed me fifteen cents. "Really, Jonathan?" she said. "Only fifteen cents?"

I said, "Yes, Ma'am, and I hope you're pleased with my work."

Mrs. Trillingham Walsh established by several more questions that my price was indeed fifteen cents, whereupon she reached in her purse and handed me fifteen cents. Now a lesser kid would have fainted dead away or told Mrs. Trillingham Walsh what to do with her crappy money. But I am proud to say that I merely backed away, offered several more thank yous, and went home bawling. But in my room a brilliant idea struck me. I wrote a short note to the sweet old lady:

Dear Mrs. Walsh,
I wanted to take this oportunity to thank you again for your business. It was my pleasure indeed to work for you. You are most considered.
Your friend,
Jonathan Rhoades

A few days later I got a letter in the mail. There was no return address. Inside was a sheet of paper and two one-dollar bills. On the paper was written: "To a fine young lad." I said to myself, "Thank you very much, Mrs. Trillingham Walsh." I held onto her account for several years after that, and she was always good for at least a half a buck.

In the summertime I introduced the same basic techniques to the lawn-mowing racket, and it worked just as well. But I must be the first person to admit that Charley had the best summertime racket going. Charley sold flowers. He got the flowers from the neighbors' flower beds: a rose here, a zinnia or two there, a few petunias at the next place, never enough to be missed. When he had accumulated a big bouquet, Charley would carry it a few blocks away and start ringing doorbells. It never took more than three or four calls for Charley to unload the whole bouquet for a quarter or a half a buck. (Out of respect for Charley, I never worked this dodge. My own floral operation consisted simply of selling little sprays of violets for a nickel; the beatific face of the poor little flower boy often unloosed a quarter or so, and there was no overhead.) Charley's whole business came to an ignominious end when he made the mistake of trying to go bigtime. He

took in Silvio Mosca as a partner, and Silvio was never too smart in the first place. Charley explained the whole operation to Silvio, and the very first day of the partnership Silvio tried to sell Mrs. Crawford a dozen of Mrs. Crawford's own hydrangeas. A couple of phone calls put the two entrepreneurs out of business.

Charley got in trouble another time over selling seed packets. He had sent away to one of those companies which enlist small boys to do their selling and then pay the small boys commissions and prizes. Charley sold twenty-four packages of seeds in about a week, and won $1.20 plus a diary with a genuine simulated leatherette binding. It was all so easy that Charley got carried away. He flipped through the company's prize catalogue and discovered that it was possible—nay, almost unavoidable—to win a bicycle. Charley wrote the company, reminded them that he was one of their star salesmen, told them he was going to win that bike, and requested that they send him the proper number of seed packets to carry off such an endeavor. Back through the mail—it seemed like the very next day—came a box barely small enough to get through our front door. It contained roughly enough seeds to reforest Nevada and part of Utah. Charley and I wrestled it into the living room, and I asked him what in the name of the H-Bar-O Ranch did he think he was going to do with all those seed packets. "Sell 'em," Charley said calmly.

I cannot in honesty say that Charley didn't give it a good try. But he had already sold seeds in our immediate neighborhood and now the market was tougher. He was calling on strangers who didn't look on him as a sweet little neighbor boy, but as just another snotty-nosed kid trying to turn a quick buck. And besides, it was early October and we had already had our first frost.

After a few days Charley had sold forty-five cents worth of seeds, and was working strange territory six blocks from home. "Give up, Charley," I said, "and send the seeds back." Charley said nothing doing; he would simply wait till the spring thaw.

The weeks went by, and the seed company's whole sequence of form letters began arriving. The first one opened with a friendly: "HI!" It pointed out that the company hadn't heard anything for awhile and was just wondering, gee whillikers, how things were going with that last shipment, by golly. Then came one beginning: "Dear Salesman: We'll bet you're just too darned busy selling seeds, but we couldn't help wondering if you would drop us a line and let us know how things are going. . . ." Charley appreciated these warm notes, but he didn't answer them because he hadn't the vaguest idea how to sell the remaining seeds (by now we had a foot of snow) or how to get the monstrous box back to the company.

Now the incoming mail began hotting up a little. "Dear Salesman: We cannot believe that you are deliberately ignoring our letters. . . ." Then: "We have a considerable investment in you, and in your integrity. . . ." And finally: "You leave us no choice but to communicate directly with your parents. If we have not heard from you within ten days. . .

Charley began to sweat, but he still had no idea what to do. Imagine his relief when, two weeks later, there came a letter addressed to Master Charles Rhoades. It began with "HI!" and went on to say that the company hadn't heard anything and was just wondering, gee whillikers, how things were going, by golly. The whole dreary sequence of letters now began again, ending two months later with another threat to write the parents. But this time the company meant business, and soon came a letter addressed to Harvey Rhoades. Charley intercepted it and composed an answer:

Gentlemen:

My son Charles Rhoades has proved himself to be a boy of real enterprize. You need have no fears that, when he returns from the hospitel, he will go out and sell your seeds with Real Enterprize.

My father,
Mr. Rhoades

The outburst that followed the exposure of all this hanky-panky is best left unreported, as it does nothing to reveal the fundamental goodness of my father. The seeds were sent back at Father's expense, but this is not to say that

Charley didn't pay a certain price, too. Let me add that my brother Charley was never one to hold a grudge, and after two or three years he began talking to Father again.

Epilogue

You may ask: Why this book? Perhaps a word about Uncle Azul, my mother's brother, will help explain. Uncle Azul had a hatred for authority in any form. He hated his teachers, his corporal in the Army, even the cop on the beat. When New York was having one of its periodic anti-litter campaigns and people were being fined twenty-five dollars for dropping cigarette ashes on the sidewalk, Uncle Azul rode down Fifth Avenue in a bus, dumped a sack of ripped-up phone books out a rear window, then quickly stepped off the bus and into a waiting car for a clean getaway, just to spite the cops. Another time New York had an anti-jaywalking campaign, and tickets were being handed out like confetti. After months of exacting preparation in a cellar in Bayonne, N.J., Uncle Azul and three confederates staked themselves out at each of the corners of Broadway and 50th Street, a block from the nearest policeman, and began an orgy of jaywalking, with two men in motion against the red light at all times. When the cop scurried down to halt this crime wave, the four vanished into the subway, only to pop up a half-hour later in the same spot. That was Uncle Azul's biggest job, and he speaks of it nowadays with understandable pride. The New York City Police Department, on the other hand, speaks of it with great shame or not at all, and very frequently denies that the incident even occurred.

You may ask what Uncle Azul does for a living, and you will be asking a frightfully interesting question there, too. Uncle Azul used to be a card-cheat by trade, being the inventor of the Hors d'Oeuvres System of Contract Bridge Bidding. One of the big problems in bridge is how to tell your partner exactly what cards you hold. Under Uncle Azul's Hors d'Oeuvres System, your partner could learn your exact holding by observing what hors d'oeuvres you ate and in what order. For example, if you ate a red caviar on Ry-Krisp, followed by two black caviars, four minced eggs without pimiento, three minced eggs with pimiento, a very large black olive, and two small ones, partner would then know that you held the ace of hearts, the ace and king of clubs, A-K-Q-J-x-x-x of diamonds, and A-x-x of spades. He would also know that you had a very good chance for grand slam, and that you were going to get fat. Eventually, the obesity factor is what put Uncle

Azul's system out of business. In 1948, when the Hors d'Oeuvres System was being taught in bridge schools all across the country, the average weight of players jumped from 161 to 193 pounds (National Bridge Council Statistics, 1948). This killed the system, as most bridge players are women.

Uncle Azul then turned to golf, and invented the so-called "Sure-putt Technique," in which you visit the greens before playing and tap green toothpicks into place so that they form invisible funnel-shaped corridors leading to the cup. Making certain to land on the far side of the green, you then offer to bet that you can hole out in one stroke. After putting out and pocketing all bets, you walk up to the cup, remove the ball, and tread all the toothpicks into the ground in one smooth, graceful motion. This is the only putting system in the world which enables you to offer eight-to-five odds that you will sink a sixty-foot putt, and it worked profitably for Uncle Azul for several years until he tangled with a big-betting, poor-shooting golfer who had the bad manners to rush up to the green and take his own putt first before Uncle Azul could stop him. The "sucker" drove the ball about seventy miles an hour right at the corridor of toothpicks, but from a broadside position. The ball hit the wall of camouflaged wood and bounced all the way off the green, leaving the golfer with a difficult chip shot. "My, my," said Uncle Azul. "That is certainly the stiffest grass I have ever seen." They charged Uncle Azul with bunco; he forfeited a $250 bond and skipped town.

For several years after that, Uncle Azul stayed in bed, resting and smoking, and his savings dwindled dangerously. Then one day in Philadelphia a stranger walked up to him and said he knew the location of fabulously rich silver deposits in Mexico; the stranger said he liked Uncle Azul's looks and wanted to cut him in on the deal; it would not cost Uncle Azul a nickel. All he had to do was put up five hundred dollars as "good faith" money; he would get back the five hundred dollars, win, lose or draw. And to eliminate any possible doubts Uncle Azul might have, the man swore to all this on the name of his sainted mother.

Who could turn down such a fair deal? Uncle Azul scraped together the last of his savings; he hocked his gold watch, and borrowed $363 from a friend, and pressed five hundred dollars into the eager hands of the kind stranger, who promptly disappeared. Two years went by and then Uncle Azul got a letter from Mexico. The mine was a big success, and enclosed was a certified check for $967,000.

Now Uncle Azul lives in a nineteen-room penthouse apartment on Park Avenue, and is considered by everyone to be a living proof that one can become rich and successful, provided one is energetic, honest, and intelligent.

But to get back to your original question: Why this book?

I don't know "why this book." If I knew the answer to that question, would I have spent five pages telling about Uncle Azul?

THE END